Suffering In Silence

The Legacy of
Unresolved Sexual Abuse

Anne Ancelin Schutzenberger

Ghislain Devroede

Foreword by Anne Teachworth

Translated from French by Anne Trager

Edited in English by Deirdre Givens

GESTALT INSTITUTE PRESS
NEW ORLEANS/METAIRIE, LA. USA

First Published in France in 2003
as *Ces enfants malades de leurs parents*
by Editions Payot

Copyright © 2005, Gestalt Institute of New Orleans, Inc.
Translated from French by Anne Trager
Published with the kind assistance of the
French Ministry of Culture, Centre national du livre

First printing, January 2005
Second printing, revised March 2007

Library of Congress catalog card number applied for.
ISBGN 1-889968 51 X

Published by
Gestalt Institute Press
1537 Metairie Road
Metairie, Louisiana 70005 USA

504 828 2267
http://www.gestaltinstitutepress.com

Emails: gestaltinstpress@aol.com
        ateachw@aol.com

Dedicated to our patients and our families
for their support of this project and of us.

Contents

Foreword

"Doctor, what's the matter with my child? Can you help us?"…Two questions frantic parents often ask the doctor when they bring their child in with a medical problem.

"Well, we'll just have to wait and see what the tests show. At first glance, I can't find any apparent medical reason for the pain," the doctor sometimes answers.

"Maybe it's just emotional, or psychosomatic. Nothing showed up on the exam. It might just be stress," is what the doctor sometimes has to say, on the first, or at least during a subsequent frustrating visit when there are no clear results from tests. However, parents often feel threatened or unfairly accused if a visit to a psychotherapist is even suggested. It is an intense moment.

In this book, Schutzenberger and Devroede explain how unfinished grief or emotional pain from a terrible tragedy in the parent or grandparent's past is often stored in the family's unconscious memory and inherited as a physical or mental health problem by a child in a following generation without any plausible medical explanation.

Often, the doctor too, for medical or legal reasons, may actually feel frustrated or accused of incompetence for being unable to give an accurate diagnosis. Physicians regularly feel pressured to quickly prescribe a medicine to stop the pain and when it doesn't work, announce, "We may have to operate." Words no doctor wants to say and no parent wants to hear. What to do when the doctor can't find the cause or the cure? Is there another explanation out there? Perhaps…

Over and over again in their private practices, Anne Schutzenberger and Ghislain Devroede have discovered that a high incidence of unexplainable medical, physical or mental problems in children are linked to unexpressed emotional pain from a previous generation's unresolved trauma. Detailing a myriad of digestive difficulties and psychosomatic problems in patients with unresolved traumas in their family history, Schutzenberger and Devroede have traced these sick children's symptoms back to secrets hidden in the "family tree."

Gradually, it has become increasingly clear to them if someone in the family's past has repressed a painful response to a trauma, their unexpressed emotions will "show up in the present as the physical or psychological pain now being suffered in silence" by their children or grandchildren.

We have long been aware of the repetitive pattern of the Cycle of Abuse wherein a parent repeats the same physical or sexual abuse that was done to him or her as a child. The case studies described in this book are not that type of direct parental abuse. These are examples of indirect, unconscious, and passive abuse. The diseases of the young patients diagnosed and treated by Schutzenberger and Devroede were "inherited," so to speak, not physically from a parent who had actually experienced the original abuse, but emotionally from their repressed response to it.

As a result of this discovery, the authors of this book are now dedicated to encouraging patients and parents to reveal and resolve these long-hidden family traumas and express long-repressed emotional responses to stop these transgenerational-induced illnesses. Both Schutzenberger and Devroede, by drawing on decades of experience in their respective fields of psychotherapy and medicine, have provided us with dramatic clinical examples of their unique psychotherapeutic approach to treating children who come to them with a variety of digestive and psychosomatic difficulties. The approach they've applied here to these children theoretically also applies to an adult population. The effectiveness of this approach remains to be demonstrated in further clinical practice.

What sets both Schutzenberger and Devroede apart as clinician researchers is their varied backgrounds in both medical and psychological services. In addition, as professional trainers, psychotherapists and university professors, they are sought out by their colleagues and former patients who now refer children and adults when their troubles are difficult to diagnose or treat using traditional therapeutic approaches.

Back in the early 80s, a psychiatrist friend of mine, Chet Scrignar, MD, first explained PTSD to me as the psychological and health-related damaging effects from withholding emotions after a traumatic event. The acronym for Post Traumatic Stress Disorder, PTSD is a term that has since become more commonly known.

In a newspaper interview following the collapse of the World Trade Center in New York City on Sept. 11, 2001, I urged the public to talk about their shock, to shiver out their fears and to cry out their sorrow. Those who could release their emotions didn't even try to hide their feelings. As a result, they openly grieved and eventually recovered from the horror, while those who couldn't, kept their pain a secret inside them. Therapists all over the United States saw a rise in the incidence of PTSD from these unexpressed emotional reactions. Stoic people were urged to express feelings to avoid subsequent somatizations. Being brave to them meant being "strong" by not showing their shock or fear.

Commenting on the recent disaster from the Tsunami of December 26, 2004, another expert on the subject, Richard Bryant, head of the Post-Traumatic Stress Disorder Unit at the University of New South Wales, said in an Internet article that trauma experienced by survivors does not always result in major psychological damage. "After a terrifying event, only about twenty-five percent of people tend to develop symptoms… The way people… respond to their experiences will depend on their mental disposition before the event and how well they can communicate their feelings afterward" (January 2, 2005, AOL News).

This is important information for people who might otherwise tend to repress their feelings of shock and grief. Indeed, somatization is the repression of emotional pain that subsequently gets "acted out" as a mental disturbance or physical symptom. Somatization is a recognizable sign of PTSD and psychosomatic illness.

However, the somatized stress response now manifesting in the patients described in this book had been repressed, not by the current victim, but by a family member in a previous generation who had long ago avoided dealing with any painful emotions from their own traumatic event or abusive situation. Unknowingly, these parents or grandparents had unconsciously transmitted their unfelt emotional pain to the next generation to feel. It's important to note here that although the original traumatic events had not happened to the sick children, the somatized illnesses were showing up in them, even though most of these children had no awareness of the parents' original trauma. This book is therefore about stopping this transgenerational somatization that had continued through the family line as a painful legacy.

In all cases sent to Schutzenberger or Devroede by other practitioners, even though the referring clinician had already taken a traditional family–of–origin or medical history from the parents, the family trauma had remained secret until the authors specifically questioned the parent(s) about "family secrets." As the authors began to realize, these "forgotten tragedies" were the psychosomatic causes. The children's sick bodies were unconsciously remembering the pain their family systems had tried to hide or forget.

Anne Schutzenberger, a group analyst, clinical social psychologist and psychodramatist in Paris, has developed a pioneer transgenerational approach to psychotherapy which has demonstrates that ungrieved emotional pain from one generation's unresolved trauma is often expressed in following generations either as a repetition of the actual event or as physical pain. The ill children described in these case studies had become mere passive links in a family chain. Be it shock or shame, illegal or immoral behaviors, the emotions or events their parents or grandparents "didn't want to talk about" had been transmitted to these young patients as a physical or psychosomatic illness.

Although most of the children described in this book were sick with various problems, neither they nor their parents had any conscious awareness that the family secret was the real source of their pain. Nevertheless, their children's bodies knew it. The next generation had indeed become innocent victims of this unconscious cycle of abuse while their family couldn't stop on their own.

Ghislain Devroede, a colorectal surgeon and Professor of surgery in Canada, gives us fascinating case studies one after the other of somatized illnesses "released" as the result of intensive questioning of parents in his medical practice. Instead of relying solely on medicine, tests or surgery, Devroede now treats his young patients by first searching for "hushed-up" events in their parents' family history that "no wants to talk about" either out loud or at all.

Using Anne Schutzenberger's transgenerational approach, he regularly uncovers long-kept family secrets that explain the emotional cause of a young patient's digestive difficulty. The remarkable case studies included here illustrate how many of his patients have recovered from their physical symptoms by his discovery of the secret parallels between their physical pain and their family's unresolved secrets.

Consistently, Devroede has found that when the parent(s) finally disclose their own childhood abuse or family secret to him, their child's physical symptoms simultaneously disappear. Using a transgenerational approach, mysteries as to why pelvic pain and gastrointestinal symptoms had appeared genetically in otherwise healthy infants and children will probably someday be solved. Inherited emotional pain from previous generations can be relieved.

By using Schutzenberger's and Devroede's work, clinicians can now trace unexplained illnesses by this same process of identifying family secrets and then facilitating the release of the long-unexpressed emotional agony often by simply having the parent or the patient say a real good-bye to a dead loved one.

Anne Schutzenberger's theory of ancestral repetitive patterns states that there is an "invisible family loyalty" owed to previous generations that may indeed predispose children to unwittingly repeat the unfelt suffering or unfinished business of a parent or grandparent in their own lifetime. Schutzenberger has spent fifty years of her life researching these phenomena and developing a corrective emotional experience whereby a family member psychodramatically replays the original event from their own past or that of an ancestor, and ends their transgenerational karma by re-enacting a new and completed positive ending to the original trauma. Basically, Schutzenberger helps her clients recreate in a group setting what is called a "surplus reality." The psychodrama re-enactment creates a new memory for the client.

As Devroede has discovered, the mysterious roots of current gastrointestinal difficulties in most of the cases they see can often be explained after methodically retracing the patient's family tree, thereby uncovering important secrets that have been "buried alive" in their unconscious memory. By obtaining an intensive family history which searches for traumas and secrets, other clinicians can also find the explanation for "coincidental" physical or emotional symptoms which have popped-up in the family generations later.

Ghislain Devroede expands on his classic scientific approach to medical problems, by adding this trauma history to his approach to resolving the family's transgenerational issues. He has observed many an illness or negative pattern enter into remission, and possibly, cured! His unique non-surgical psychotherapeutic approach actually releases painful emotions hiding in the family tree.

Repeatedly, the cycle of somatization usually ends when the parent recognizes that the recurring family trauma being represented in their child is now begging for release from the transgenerational closet. Incredibly, once the family secret has been admitted and the repressed words or feelings are expressed by the parent, the illness in the child often fades away, even if the child is not present during the admission or never hears about the secret.

This is amazing evidence that appears to support Rupert Sheldrake's (1995) theory of the invisible energy connections which exist in a family's morphogenetic field, and especially between people who have strong feelings for each other (Sheldrake, 1995).

As mere links in a chain of generations, children may have no freedom of choice in some of the health problems their ancestors have visited upon them, but Professors Schutzenberger and Devroede's transgenerational approach can help many parents put an end to their child's somatized family karma once and for all without surgery. Remarkably, 'the truth will not only set you free,' it can also set your children free.

The goal of this book is to inform all parents that they can stop these transgenerational repetitions in their offspring by revealing the family secret to the clinician, and/or to the child/patient, but, and even more importantly, to inform all clinicians to ask patients these types of questions.

Schutzenberger and Devroede present some preliminary fascinating case studies of patients who have conquered physical difficulties by discovering parallels between their own health and the secrets kept by their forbearers. This book offers a unique method to end the cycle of transgenerational abuse. It is now literally very "A— Parent" that family secrets can offer another explanation for somatized "disease." The release of repressed emotional energy that had remained locked away within the family's secret may be the best medicine to arrest the disease.

Schutzenberger and Devroede believe it is of the utmost importance that people release their hidden emotional pain before they or their children can truly heal. Anne Schutzenberger gives examples of Psychodrama reenactments in this book that will tell you, the reader, exactly how to do that for yourself or your family.

For years, people have been congratulated for "being strong" in times of loss and for "keeping family matters secret" in the face of adversity, but "suffering in silence" should never be considered a courageous or effective way to handle trauma. We know from many medical sources that repressed emotions have caused physical symptoms in the traumatized person. We are just now becoming aware that unresolved emotional issues are often transmitted to the next generation "as is," unresolved!

Indeed, 'sticks and stones will break your bones,' and words can definitely hurt you, but not crying out the emotional pain from the traumatic event may not just hurt you, but also hurt the next generation. We can thus truly state that people will rarely die from too much crying it out and mourning. They might, however, be deadened by denial or repression of the sadness, or the emotional exhaustion of depression, but not from crying. As we have shown, illness often results from repressing the hurt inflicted by severe traumas, particularly those hurts that have a strong emotional component.

Schutzenberger and Devroede offer a very simple coping strategy to stop this painful legacy. The act of taking the "skeleton out of the family closet" can allow the next generation to escape the onset of an actual disease, and put a stop to the unnecessary and all too frequent repetitions of somatized emotions that make no sense from a one dimensional medical point of view.

I can truly summarize the lesson in this book into this one sentence… "If you don't feel, you don't heal."

January 11, 2005

Anne Teachworth, Publisher
Gestalt Institute Press
New Orleans, La. USA

Introduction

"The fathers have eaten sour grapes, and the children's teeth are set on edge."

The Bible, Jeremiah, 31:29

All children resonate with their parents — for better or worse. The resonance can be harmonious, and the baby will blossom like a flower; but a child will also reflect a troubled mother, or one in grieving, or one who is too exhausted. Therefore, it is hardly surprising that unresolved family problems, traumas or secrets lead to suffering in offspring.

We were raised by adults: by our two parents if they stayed together; if not, by one of them, or by our grandparents, or by substitute parents, or perhaps by social workers employed in orphanages or other places. Their problems, their distress, their traumatisms, their silences and secrets marked us more than we realize, and in any case more than the adults know or are willing to admit.

Some traumas have been silenced because they are too harsh, unspeakable. Parents or grandparents did not assimilate them, metabolize them or voice them. A secret formed, weighing down the shoulders of the future generations, a secret capable of provoking somatic disorders in children—at least that is our hypothesis.

Most children had parents good enough to allow them to live, or they figured out how to manage (resilient children). This is not the case for all children. Children who are sick from their parents suffer intensely and in many different ways during their childhood, and then later when they become adults themselves. For example, many experience stomachaches that ruin their lives. In fact, we know today that digestive disorders and pain are often linked to family traumatisms, including sexual abuse. But other types of pain can be linked to parents who carry war traumas, poorly buried deaths or unfinished grieving, emotional deprivation, or brutal separations due to internment, a mother or father's serious illness or worse, their death.

Often, these children will repeat the symptoms of the parent from which they were separated when their own children reach the age they were at the time of the initial trauma. In these cases, we speak of the Anniversary Syndrome, which Anne Ancelin Schützenberger demonstrated could repeat itself from generation to generation. Ultimately, the question is not whether it is the fault of the parents. They did what they could, with the means they had available to them, and looking for a guilty party serves no purpose. Moreover, sometimes we find that the initial problems and traumas lie in the lives of the great grandparents. The fact remains that the children suffer, often over several generations. They suffer in their minds, but also in their bodies. Their "teeth are set on edge" because their parents "have eaten sour grapes."

We have based this book on the results of the scientific studies listed at the end of this book (along with a glossary that explains, among other things, the medical and technical terms we use). We have also based it on observations made in our respective practices. It contains known, proven and irrefutable facts, along with leads, insights and hypotheses where reliable data was not available.

There is a lot of mention of the abdomen, the belly, in the pages that follow. The abdomen serves as an example, because bellyaches are so common, and we will come back to it in the conclusion. We will also discuss sexual abuse, but there again; we hope not to limit our discussion to this kind of example. In some cases, when a parent was a victim of sexual abuse during his or her own childhood and has never talked about it, we find his or her own child suffers from functional digestive disorders. Other of these children are always hyper-alert, always ready to react, their muscles much too tense. More striking, some heal suddenly when the parent in question begins therapy to overcome his or her own pain.

We know psychological pain can be transmitted over several generations. In this book, we want to demonstrate that this kind of transmission can also apply to bodily dysfunctions. When things go unspoken, sometimes the body can express them: this is somatization. In this case, the child's body, or the grandchild's or the great grandchild's, whatever their age, becomes the language for the wounded ancestors, the "words" for that ancestor's trauma.

As a result, it becomes necessary to "get the skeletons out of the closet," to decode and to heal the still-open wounds in order to finally be liberated from the chill carried inside.

Chapter I

The Child's Body, "Words" for the Parents' Past

Children Who Learn To Be Sick!

In 2001, R. L. Levy and his colleagues demonstrated that children can *learn* to have bellyaches, constipation and diarrhea. They do so in an attempt to imitate, in their bodies, the things their parents suffered from. This study, which was based on a group of more than 15,000 pairs of identical and fraternal twins and their parents, proves that our environment takes on at least as much importance in the genesis of these functional gastrointestinal disorders as our physical, genetic and hereditary characteristics (Levy, Jones, Whitehead, Feld, Talley, 2000; 2001).

Some babies are constipated *from birth*. Their disorder is not organic; they do not suffer from a congenital disease such as Hirschsprung's Disease, which requires surgery (Watier, Feldman, Arhan, Devroede, 1995 and Martelli, 1998). Nor is their disorder related to their food intake. In these cases, an event seems to have occurred during birth, or even earlier while they were still in the womb, that had an impact on their digestive tract. It is as if their bodies were expressing something much more comprehensive and psychosomatic. When one measures their anal and rectal motility, these children show no differences from others who develop this kind of constipation later, when it is clearly linked to toilet training.

There is a third piece of related information. This time, it concerns adults: fifty percent of women who suffer from Irritable Bowel Syndrome were abused during their childhood, two thirds of them prior to the age of fourteen. In addition, one finds more histories of sexual abuse in people who suffer from functional disorders of the lower digestive tract (colon, rectum, and anus) than among those whose disorders are found in the upper digestive tract (esophagus, stomach). These three pieces of information will help us to understand what follows.

Freud, Sexual Abuse and False Memories

For a long time, nobody—not even doctors!—wanted to hear about children's hardships or pain. Everyone agreed to deny the existence of sexual abuse. Freud himself avoided speaking frankly about the subject. Shrinking back from the incest stories he was hearing, he preferred to develop the Oedipus Complex, "forgetting" that Oedipus did not kill his father, Laios, with the intention of sleeping with his mother, Jocasta.

Freud dodged another equally crucial fact. Oedipus did not know Laios was his father until after he killed him. Laios, who was an orphan, had been taken in by a king who already had a son, and Laios killed the son after having homosexual relations with him. As a result, the gods condemned him to never have children, and if he did, his son would be fated to kill him and make love to his wife. When Laios fathered Oedipus, he remembered this prophecy. He and Jocasta decided to kill the newborn by "exposing him," that is, by abandoning him on the mountain, hung by his feet, to be devoured by wild animals. Oedipus's feet swelled, he developed edemas, thus explaining the name Oedipus, which means "he with swollen feet."

Later, when Oedipus discovered that he was "guilty" of having killed his father and having slept with his mother, he punished himself. Did he follow the customs of his era and cut off his right hand, with which he inadvertently killed his father? No. Did he cut off his sexual organ, after sleeping with Jocasta not knowing she was his mother (and having several children with her)? No, he did not do that either. Oedipus clawed out his own eyes. When he thought about what he had endured, he understood that his greatest error was that he had not seen the family and personal story he had fallen into, nor had he seen that he came from a family whose members had been stuck in this kind of problem for several generations (Freud, 1913, 1923, 1919).

And what parents they were: egotistical, unfair and criminal. With this, Freud transformed his observations into a theory about fantasies, according to which a child could "invent" a story about sexual abuse! Factually speaking, such a stance comes down to taking sides with the abusers against the abused. Did he think, then, that parents were always right and children always wrong? We know this is not true, yet in a way this is what fantasy theory—which is often "pasted" onto cases of actual abuse—implies. Moreover, this theory contributes to perpetuating a process of "re-victimization," which is extremely frequent among victims of sexual abuse, who will go from abuser to abuser (Freud, 1999/1907b; 1999/1900; 1999/1908, 1999/1996).

To suggest a link between sexual abuse and symptoms as banal as chronic abdominal pain, constipation and diarrhea, which are the basic symptoms of Irritable Bowel Syndrome, is to come up against similar denial mechanisms. Quebec made a lot of progress in this regard with the creation of the Office of Youth Protection. Laws changed so that no person making a claim of sexual abuse, even a false one or one based only on malicious suspicions, could be charged with defamation. In France, recent efforts have been made in the same direction. Confidentiality of investigations is meant to protect the pseudo-abusers. The result has been an exponential increase in the number of sexual abuse claims.

The most flagrant proof of sexual abuse is quite obviously when the offender recognizes his faults. In these cases, it is very clear that the fantasy theory does not apply and is non-operational. Although less convincing, a judicial demonstration that abuse actually occurred can substitute for a confession. Then there are situations where the abuser does not recognize his faults and the police do not manage to prove that abuse has occurred. Here we enter more fuzzy territory, when it is difficult to demonstrate that abuse occurred.

It is important here to remember that at one time therapists literally suggested to people that they had been abused, even when those people had not made any such claims. As a result, a theory of "false memories" developed, which suggests that the caretaker's influence induces pseudo-memories of sexual abuse. Unfortunately, false accusations of incest have also been used in certain divorce cases.

Who Lies The Least?

The body is more reliable than our memory: it is medically possible to find bodily traces of past sexual abuse (Leroi AM, Bernier 1995, Leroi AM, Berkelmans, 1995). It becomes much more difficult to allege false memories if the body remembers, and if abused subjects differ in their bodies from those not abused. A good example is that of anismus. This anomaly is an excellent indicator of a history of sexual abuse. What is it? Normally, when a person strains to defecate, the anus relaxes to let the stool through. In the case of anismus, the inverse occurs: the anus contracts instead of opening.

Almost all women who have been sexually abused suffer from anismus. Evidently, this does not mean that the contrary is true; some subjects with anismus have never been abused. Nevertheless, we know that among cases of anismus, there are ten times more histories of sexual abuse than when there is no anismus.

As a result, this clinical sign becomes very useful for medical practitioners, as the wide majority of doctors perform a digital rectal examination at one time or another. The doctor needs only to add a simple request during the examination, which is to strain as if going to the bathroom. If the patient contracts the anus while straining, the doctor can diagnose anismus and suppose that the probability of sexual abuse is high.

Evidently, you cannot be certain sexual abuse occurred without explicitly asking the question. As it is the body transmitting the information, it is no necessary to ask the question at the precise moment of the examination. The practitioner could wait for an easier moment, once a relationship of trust has been established.

Anal penetration that causes abdominal pain can also be evidence of sexual abuse. This still requires scientific confirmation, but it is an interesting lead, in that anal penetration is part of numerous medical examinations, such as the digital rectal exam, proctoscopy, colonoscopy, and barium enema. A clinician should be alerted to the possibility of past abuse if the penetration causes abdominal pain, because in this case, for there to be an abdominal reaction, the message was necessarily received in the brain, which caused a reaction in the abdomen, the latter not being in direct neurological communication with the anal canal.

Anismus is a somatic dissociation. One part of the brain sends a message to strain, to increase pressure in the rectum in order to try to defecate, while another part of the brain sends the opposite order: contract so as not to defecate. It is not really surprising to find this kind of dissociation in victims of sexual abuse, because such victims frequently dissociate psychologically in order not to suffer again as much as they suffered at the time of the sexual abuse.

This is the case of the woman who had a panic attack every time she saw a certain type of wallpaper. One day, she remembered the wallpaper in the room where her father had raped her when she was little. She had plunged her thoughts into the wallpaper in order to no longer feel that pain. The personality split into two parts, one a suffering victim and one a non-suffering observer, more or less present at the scene of the crime.

Dissociation can lead to resilience, because the observing part will grow, while the suffering part sinks into chaos and dependence. The relatively healthy and untouched part of the individual can take three courses of action: lying, mythomania, or dreaming. In the three cases, it is a question of providing the individual with a feeling of safety. Lying serves to mask reality and to protect, like a wall. Mythomania serves to compensate for emptiness and to protect, like a seductive image—a mythomaniac lies with every breath, because if he stops lying, he'll stop breathing.

Dreaming gives shape to an ideal self and creates a strong demand in the dreamer to transform his or her life, like a drawbridge that lowers onto the open countryside. If there is no countryside, the drawbridge serves no purpose, and the child remains a prisoner of what he has invented. A relationship to another person, to family, or to society can transform dreaming into creativity or, on the contrary, into a mirage.

This is the lot of sexual abuse victims, who suffer from the devastating trauma caused by the non-recognition of their otherness and the use of their body in the place of love, which equals a psychological death. Nevertheless, some resilient subjects are capable of overcoming the traumatism. Yet they remain fragile, their resilience being built on a weakness.

There is another psychological counterpart to the physiological phenomenon of anismus. The psychoanalysts and anthropologists of the Palo Alto School studied the impact of two simultaneous contradictory messages, calling this phenomenon a "double bind." It can be found among mothers of schizophrenic children. When a mother or a maternal image sends two messages at the same time, both imperative yet completely opposite, and the father or father image is physically or mentally absent, the order cannot be stopped, because there is no counterpart to the person who gave it.

The contradictory injunction is internalized as a result, along with an impossibility for the child to comment on it to the abusing parents. This child becomes frozen and immobile. One patient made this enlightening comment about her mother: "She pushed me to be self-assured but at the same time, she always wanted to be right, telling me that she was the one who had more experience."

It is easy to draw a parallel with the double message of anismus: you have to open the anus to defecate and close it at the same time to protect against penetration and the bodily invasion of sexual abuse, or to express the fear that abuse causes. Note here that these contradictory messages raise a question. Anismus resembles vaginismus, yet in the latter; one shuts off penetration, whereas in the former, one shuts off expulsion.

Psychoanalysts have taught us that unconscious body representations equate the penis, the stool and the fetus. Research in this direction could probably lead to a better understanding of the genesis of anismus in cases of sexual abuse.

Somatization And Factitious Disorders

Somatization and imagination are not the same thing. Yet, people often confuse the two. When doctors explain to patients that they suffer from functional gastrointestinal disorders, sometimes the patients respond, "That's right, you're just like the others. You think it's all in my head!" Somatization occurs when painful emotions are expressed solely through the body. It is a real disorder. On the other hand, the imagination is at work in factitious disorders. Take the following example. A nurse around the age of 50 consulted her doctor about her fatigue and was found to have hypochromic anemia caused by a lack and loss of iron. As this kind of anemia is most often caused by abundant menstruation, her doctor looked into her genital physiology to find she was no longer menstruating: she had had her uterus removed.

This left the doctor to find another source of the lost blood. The other most frequent cause of hypochromic anemia, in addition to menstruation, is a low-level loss of blood in the digestive tract. Given the patient's age, the doctor thought there may be cancer of the caecum, in the right side of the colon, where the diameter is large enough for a person to lose blood without experiencing other symptoms. As a matter of fact, the patient's stool contained blood. The necessary endoscopy and x-ray examinations were performed, but against all expectations, the large intestine was perfectly normal. There was no colon cancer.

Considering the blood loss, hypochromic anemia and lack of iron, the clinician wondered if the cause could be an injury located higher up in the digestive tract. But again, the esophagus, the stomach and the small intestine were all normal. He again verified the blood count and the gastrointestinal blood loss, which were confirmed.

What was the key to the mystery? The patient left her room one day to have an x-ray, and staff found syringes full of blood in her closet. She was pumping out her own blood and drinking it! This explains the hypochromic anemia and the bloody stool. But why?

This is a factitious disorder: an imaginary illness. Somatization is very different. The bond between the mind and the body occurs through psycho-physiological links during situations of extreme crisis, and through psycho-neuro-immunologic channels when stress is chronic. The response to post-traumatic stress includes two physiologic mechanisms. For example, anger—not an illness—causes the colon to contract and the stomach to relax (Welgan, 1988,2000). It's logical: a dangerous situation (anger indicates the possibility of a fight) is not the time to vomit or to defecate.

So, contractions close off the colon and the gastric antrum inhibition relaxes the stomach. This reaction occurs to a much greater degree in subjects suffering from Irritable Bowel Syndrome (IBS). Moreover, the latter have great difficulties in expressing their emotions (Drossman, 1988). It is not that the IBS patients suffer from stress more often than a normal subject, but when you ask them to indicate the gravity of a stressful situation, they tend to say, "It's nothing" and dismiss the full impact of what has happened to them. Rather than getting angry, these subjects will somatize in the stomach and the colon.

Social psychologists, psychoanalysts and osteopaths have studied anger and concur that it is an important factor in psychosomatic reactions, particularly in those linked to a subject's personal past and their approach to life events. Feminist family therapists invented the term "dance of anger" to describe repetitive, difficult family relationships. Children easily associate anger with things that are unfair, which is how they describe rape, incest, sexual abuse, beatings or any other form of family or social abuse.

IBS patients also talk about the injustice they have suffered from tragic family deaths at a young age, or from various other family troubles, and also from family secrets that are impossible to assimilate. Consequently, since the beginning of last century, the term "unfinished business" has been used to describe what remains in the mind and the memory in these cases. Recently, many studies have led to a better understanding of the inheritance of family maledictions. It has even been demonstrated that coincidences can occur at the same age a patient was at the time of their parent's precocious death and the age of that patient's own child at the time of that patient's death (Hilgard,). The wounded–child–now–adult may be hospitalized for mental illness when his own child reaches the age he was when his own parent died. There is significant statistical evidence of such links. In these cases, it is also possible to find similar imitative symptoms or syndromes.

Intergenerational links can be found in family unhappiness, dysfunctions and traumatisms, just as in the unfinished business of injustice, anger and traumatic deaths. Could it be possible to find similar links where there is somatization among descendants, given that post-traumatic stress causes a lot of somatization and that victims of traumas are not all capable of repairing the resulting psychological damages in their lifetimes, and certainly not prior to having conceived children?

Chapter II

Family Secrets

There are secrets, and there are secrets. Everyone has the right to a secret garden and to intimacy. Everyone has the right and the duty to preserve privacy—even from his or her own family. Nobody owes the whole truth to anyone (except, of course, in the confessional or in a judicial investigation).

But to keep a secret for the children's good is to do them wrong. Family secrets can be devastating. Murder, rape, incest, abortion, bankruptcy, drunkenness, mental illness, incarceration, ethnic origin, political or religious associations… whatever the shame attached to an event kept secret, it is much smaller than what the children and grandchildren will imagine when they look for the truth. Many things considered normal today (such as a birth before marriage) caused scandals during the nineteenth and twentieth centuries and were concealed even from other family members.

Storing Up Pain

A weighty, unconscious, invisible family loyalty can lead certain individuals to be sensitive to events that occurred in their family at a certain age, on a certain date, or during a certain period. They can become vulnerable at those times to the point of falling ill or having an accident themselves; the woman who develops a mental illness when her child reaches the age that she herself was the day her own mother died tragically. But people do not only express themselves through their minds.

We express ourselves with words, and body language, mimicking, posture, clothing, sexuality, emotions, the use of space and time... and through our silences. Communication also occurs through small injuries, symptoms and illnesses. And these events have helped us to understand what is today called a secondary gain from an illness.

If a person, willingly or not, had to develop a stoic attitude when faced with the physical pain of his childhood, he or she will tend to ignore abnormal body symptoms, to the point of becoming suddenly and severely ill when a crisis occurs and is not recognized as one.

Quite the opposite, when a child only received attention from his parents when he was ill, that child will consider illness to be an asset equivalent to the satisfaction of a need for immediate attention. You should always look for the meaning behind pathology. Often, the meaning is hidden, and sometimes it is impossible to find. Yet, that should not stop you from trying; fate cannot be a disease's only cause.

Sexual abuse in any form, incestuous or extra-familial, is always tragic for the victim. Nobody can deny that. If the child grows up in a healthy environment, he could demonstrate resilience and develop the capacity to recover from his wounds, as Boris Cyrulnik (1999) clearly demonstrated in *Un Merveilleux Malheur*.

In cases of sexual abuse, the risk of serious consequences depends a great deal on environment. Influencing factors include how young the child was when the crime occurred (younger than ten), how physically violent the abuse was, how often it was repeated, whether there was a family bond with the abuser, and above all, whether the child had an opportunity (used or not) to find consolation—or, at least, to have the act, the abuse, recognized. Only one option exists when the child does not have this opportunity or when the trauma of abuse is denied and the child accused of lying, telling stories, exaggerating, or Oedipus Complex fantasies, as was for so long the case. All that is left is to store up the pain.

We know that Post-Traumatic Stress Disorder (PTSD) can occur following violent physical traumas, such as war injuries or serious accidents. PTSD also defines abuse. As a general rule, the way a person functions on the whole, both mentally and physically, is thrown off balance, which implies that a certain notion of precarious balance existing prior to the aggression or trauma disappears afterwards, and that this preexisting balance cannot be easily recovered. For example, after a car accident, it is important to ask the victim if he or she has recurring nightmares of the accident.

This occurs more frequently than imagined, even if most doctors and surgeons do not question accident victims about it. However, there is a whole process of actual bereavement that has to occur during the weeks and months that follow an accident, during which the subject learns to integrate and to manage, on an unconscious level, what he or she experienced as a dramatic invasion of his or her personal space. It is therefore easy to understand how a child, who has been sexually abused in a pernicious environment and could not find consolation or be recognized as having been abused, then transforms the overall memory of the crime into a family secret.

When the child becomes an adult, he has the possibility of freeing himself from family bonds, and therefore of confiding in people outside the family circle—professional therapists or personal relations—who allow him to air the emotional memory of these traumatisms. Next is the question of the nature of deep healing that allows for the memory of the sexual abuse to become purely factual and not charged with the unexpressed emotions felt at the time of the aggression. It is relatively rare that this bereavement process can be fully accomplished during a victim's lifetime, prior to the conception of a child and that child's intra-uterine life.

For example, when a woman has been sexually abused, she runs a large risk of having to undergo a Cesarean section because the passage through the genitals is largely handicapped by marked tissue hypertonia. We also know that mother and fetus sleep at about the same time and, in particular, when a mother dreams, her fetus dreams also. We do not know whether the mother and fetus dream of the same thing, but we can put forth the hypothesis that an unconscious transmission of past trauma could occur between them during these periods of synchronous dreaming. Unfortunately, it is impossible to scientifically prove this hypothesis.

In a worst-case scenario, twenty percent of the population has a history of sexual abuse, which does not represent a majority of the population. Even among subjects suffering from Irritable Bowel Syndrome, which is also present in twenty percent of the population according to epidemiological studies, the prevalence of sexual abuse, on either side of the Atlantic, is "only" fifty percent.

But as we have seen, the advantage of discovering past sexual abuse in the genesis of a physical pathology, whatever it may be, is that the legal definition of the abuse is reasonably precise and limited (Bagley, 1984). It does not encompass innocent games played at the dawn of sexuality, but is defined as an act imposed by a dominant figure, and not one that occurs between children in the process of exploring their sexuality together ("playing doctor"). It also involves a body part clearly linked to sexuality.

The precision of this definition notably means that if an incestuous father tells to his daughter that he wants to have sexual relations with her, and she refuses him, the courts will not consider this to be sexual abuse as long as the father respected the daughter's decision, even if his desire was clearly incestuous. Similarly, even if the diagnosis of past sexual abuse can only occur today by going back in time, that abuse, based on the precise limitations of the definition, can be established as having occurred a long time ago.

As a result, it is interesting to discover an association between digestive pathology and long-hidden past sexual abuse when it is a question of the transmission of a traumatic legacy to future generations. Sexual abuse of children is only the indicator of a deeper pathology that touches one's relationship to others and that is much more serious than physical aggression itself. Two stories give insight into this lead.

The Family That Didn't Defecate

We had known Charles for nearly ten years, but we had not seen him for more than seven years when we contacted his parents again. At the time of the survey, his parents were divorced. The child lived with his mother. We wanted to evaluate the long-term results of a physical therapy technique known as biofeedback for learning continence and defecation.

As previously stated, when a patient suffers from anismus, he contracts his anus rather than relaxing it. It is possible to measure this contraction with an electronic instrument. The instrument emits a sound that becomes higher and higher with contraction or, for children it shows a little person that climbs a staircase instead of going down. It is also possible to measure it electrically with traces of a needle that rises when the perineum contracts and lowers when it relaxes.

Charles's mother told us that her son was completely cured of his constipation. What she told us about his recovery process surprised us. None of the practitioners involved in his case had been successful, and biofeedback had not worked. Charles was suddenly cured when his mother started psychotherapy. She had hidden from us—and for that matter had never spoken about it to anyone—that she had been the victim of a major aggression when she was five years old: a priest, who was a friend of the family, attempted to rape her.

Her father walked in on the priest as he readied to commit the crime, thus saving his daughter from the rape. But her father immediately asked her not to mention the incident to anyone, as he feared a scandal. She never dared disobey.

Her own mother would hardly have been the one to lend her a compassionate ear, as she beat her daughter regularly. When we heard this story, we retraced Charles's past.

He was seven when his parents brought him in for a problem of severe constipation. His constipation had begun long before his toilet training. According to his mother, Charles had always been constipated, ever since birth. We managed to find his infancy records, which showed that he was already constipated on the second day of his short life. He therefore suffered from a problem of functional neonatal constipation (Martelli, 1998).

At the age of one month, his bowels moved only once a week. His stool became very hard when he stopped breastfeeding and began the bottle. The problem got worse with time, and towards the age of five, he started to have only one gigantic bowel movement every two weeks, which often clogged the toilets. Stories of huge stools, reflecting a mega- or too-large rectum, stopping up toilets are rare in Europe, where the pipes that carry excrements to the sewers are much larger than in North America. Charles had to make extenuating efforts in order to defecate, an ordeal that caused him a lot pain in his small behind. He also leaked incontinent liquid stools three times a day, but, as is the case with this condition called encopresis, the incontinence disappeared for a few days every time he managed to defecate.

When Charles was constipated for a period of time, he began to experience abdominal pain and to vomit. In addition, he suffered from asthma every time he was emotionally moved.

Charles was the second of three children. The pregnancy

had been difficult. Labor started prematurely at twenty-nine weeks. He hadn't done his time. His mother spoke about the pregnancy in very surprising terms: "I had been asked to hold back during my pregnancy. I kept talking to the baby in my womb: 'Come on, baby, let's close up the orifices!' Could I have sent him the wrong message?" However, she did not give a rational explanation for the association between the fact that she had to hold back from giving birth and the fact that the baby held back from defecating.

Perhaps this is an example of "cloacal thought," where the "behind" and the "front side" are mixed up in an intergenerational and fusional bond between the mother and her child. In any case, the mother thought she could have involuntarily taught her child how to become constipated. This may have been the case.

Various pediatricians, gastroenterologists and surgeons saw the child at a very young age. The decision was made to perform an anorectal manometry to look for any congenital cause of the constipation, notably Hirschsprung's Disease. The examination showed the presence of a rectoanal inhibitory reflex. In simple terms, when the rectum of a normal subject is distended, the anus relaxes, and that relaxation can be measured. This reflex does not exist in this congenital disease where there are no nerve cells in the last part of the intestine and anus. In these cases, only surgery can resolve the problem and any attempt at psychotherapy would lead to failure.

As he did not have Hirschsprung's Disease, Charles underwent various therapeutic approaches, but to no avail. He was able to control his bladder at the age of two. He began to talk and walk at a normal age. He was a little timid but he worked well at school. His father was a little bit tough on him when he was incontinent but he congratulated his son on the manly size of his stools! When the child was seven — the age of reason — he still suffered from, or at least experienced, the same problem, and his parents became desperate. At this point, they accepted the idea that perhaps a psychological problem was at play.

The child underwent a whole array of medical tests. Examinations of the anus and rectum showed that the anus was extremely tight and that, when Charles was asked to strain, the anal sphincter contracted, which is a characteristic of anismus. The large intestine was extended through to the anus; it was elongated, twisted and full of feces. When given barium to visualize the shape of the intestine, evacuation was very incomplete. The transit time through the large intestine of radiopaque markers, visible with x-rays, was normal in the right part of the colon, but slows in the left part, and notably in the rectum.

Based on this extensive medical evaluation, we concluded that there was a problem of constipation linked to Irritable Bowel Syndrome, as well as the presence of anismus leading to a distention and insensitivity of the rectum. We asked "*the*" question, as several indications of sexual abuse had been present in the anorectal manometry, and we were told that Charles had never been sexually abused.

As soon as Charles started therapy, he began having bowel movements every two or three days—a great improvement. The mother's language was as fusional as ever; when she talked about him, she often said, "We are less constipated." It took a little bit of time to distinguish between her and her child. He began to have sensations in his rectum, which he had not had previously. He also became more quick-tempered.

His parents got divorced. However, they reconstituted the family in order to be together for the child's doctor's appointments. Then something strange happened. Something obvious, actually. Charles remained constipated when he was with his mother. But not when he lived with his father!

The mother, as the self-respecting mother she was, questioned herself and stated, rather eloquently: "I think that I am a problem for my child. When Mom is feeling OK, the child is OK, and vice versa." She decided to start therapy. One subject caused a very intense emotional catharsis: she had never felt accepted as a child, as a woman, and also when she was little. It was her mother who ran the household. She declared that she had been subjected to emotional and psychological incest by her father, but denied having a history of sexual abuse. She also tried to find out about her parents' sexuality. She thought it was a shame that her own mother refused to talk to her about her childhood, and every time she tried to get the story out of her mother, the latter fell asleep instantly. This led her to believe that her mother did not love her.

This process brought with it deep questioning concerning her relationship with her own parents. She began to look at them from an adult's perspective, something she had never done before. She remembered old memories of sleeping with her father every time her mother was not there. Her anger towards her mother reached a peak when her mother, without any explanation, started attending meetings of a support group for sexually abused women.

Charles's mother also said that her parents acted very

strangely towards anything that had to do with defecation. Not only had she been constipated all of her life but, she said in her family the children were required to be constipated! Every time the children had soft stool, their parents gave them something to constipate them. This family nearly forbade defecation which explained why Charles's mother had panic attacks every time she had a bowel movement.

Charles responded to his mother's progress. For a period of time, when she was not constipated, Charles was, and vice versa. Afterwards, the mother's intestinal habits became normal, but the child remained constipated. As we said, he became increasingly angry.

One day, he stabbed a knife into his mother's kitchen table, crying out that she stole his life when she left his father and verbalizing, literally, that he would not be constipated if his parents had stayed together. He also accused her of having forced him to be born and to live.

During this critical period, Charles drew several drawings. His mother did as well. They both had separate appointments on the same day. Once, mother and son brought in remarkably similar drawings. The mother's showed a gigantic phallic mushroom, full of nudes. She had also drawn on the mushroom a number of erect penises, referring very clearly to the sexual abuse attempt by the priest. The same day, Charles, who was unaware of the story, had drawn a "smelly mushroom," whose shape strangely resembled that of the mushroom his mother had drawn, but it did not contain nudes or erect penises.

The two parents started other relationships. The mother noted that she had abdominal pain every time she had sex with her lover, something common among people with Irritable Bowel Syndrome. Also, for the first time in her life, she started crying when she reached orgasm. During her appointments, she spoke openly about her sexuality in the presence of her son and her ex-husband, without holding anything back and without modesty. She also noted that beforehand, the abdominal pain she had had during and after coitus occurred only with men with whom she did not have any emotional bond.

Charles's father had a brief relationship with a woman a lot older than he was who left him quite quickly. The pain of this separation led him to therapy. It was at this point that their appointments stopped altogether for more than seven years. That was five years ago. Charles is no longer constipated, nor does he have asthma attacks.

All Children Want To Heal Their Parents

Here is the story of Jack, who helped his mother recover by unconsciously refusing to heal.

Jack was treated by biofeedback for anismus associated with a problem of constipation that began at birth, along with serious anal incontinence and very frequent periods of fecal impaction, where the rectum became full of hard fecal matter, a condition which repeatedly required enemas to unstop him. Jack was now sixteen. This problem led him to consult a doctor. An anorectal manometry showed he had a very strong perineum, and the teenager was able to contract harder than an average patient.

His rectum was immense and insensitive. Fourteen sessions of biofeedback had no effect.

Jack's mother, Julie, developed a trusting relationship with her son's biofeedback technician, confiding in her that she often had stomachaches. She had refused to be operated on by an arrogant surgeon who had said to her, even before he examined her that she was complaining for nothing. He suggested she have a colectomy, that is, have part of her large intestine removed, because he diagnosed diverticulitis, an inflammation that occurs when too much internal pressure causes the perforation of a small hernia in the colon.

Jack's biofeedback technician encouraged Julie to consult another doctor for her problem. It turned out that she had a record of proven incidents of diverticulitis, none with complications or actual abscesses. Diverticulosis in itself is banal, frequent and in more than fifty percent of people over the age of fifty. Pouches or protrusions, like hernias, bulge out of the large intestine. If one of the pouches breaks, the fecal matter in the intestine enters into direct contact with the peritoneum, leading to diverticulitis. Rules are then defined to know when to intervene surgically.

Diverticulitis is the final product of diverticulosis, and it has been proven that diverticulosis is more common among those who suffer from Irritable Bowel Syndrome (IBS). The only treatments known today to lead to improvement in cases of IBS are psychotherapy and hypnosis.

Nevertheless, the new doctor looked for medical treatments based on the different IBS types: with diarrhea, with constipation and with the alternating of the two. After questioning, the doctor discovered that Julie's first episode of well-established diverticulitis occurred at the time of an uncle's burial. This uncle, her mother's brother, had raped her, with full vaginal penetration, when she was seven years old.

She immediately mentioned it to her mother, who forbade her to mention the incident to her father for fear the father would kill the rapist, who was living with them. The uncle was slightly mentally handicapped. So Julie didn't speak about the rape. She had a very poor relationship with her mother and adored her father, to whom, she admitted, she clung.

As soon as Julie talked to us about the rape, her son Jack instantly recovered from his constipation, without having been present or even aware of the story. Today, he no longer needs laxatives or enemas. To be safe, an extensive medical examination was nevertheless made of Julie's past diverticulitis, which showed nothing more than a diverticulosis without complications. Julie is in good health. As for her mother, Jack's grandmother, we later learned that she too had been a rape victim.

Beware Of Over-Simplification

As spectacular as they are, the stories we have just told are not necessarily representative of the norm, and we are aware of this. It would be naïve to think that a mere parental confession could cure a child in every case. Nothing is ever simple in medicine, as we see in the following case.

Melanie was six years old. She suffered from encopresis,

severe constipation with fecal impaction, and anal incontinence. At the consultation, her mother Marie explained that Melanie had not been constipated since birth, but since the age of six months, when she was severed from her mother's milk and began the bottle. Perhaps this transition has some significance in this case, as Melanie was not cured once her mother revealed that she had been sexually abused as a child. Proof would require many studies to distinguish if the functional constipation began at birth or not.

At the time of the consultation, Melanie had bowel movements once a week with immense stools, although they did not block up the toilet as in the case of Charles. The girl had abdominal pain and occasional anal fissures when she was constipated for a long period of time. Her incontinence began at the age of two and a half when her little brother was born. Melanie had seen many pediatricians and followed several treatments without the slightest success.

The little girl was extremely timid, isolated and quiet. She was obese and her hair was cut like a boy's. She remained immobile on her mother's knee and turned away from the doctor, refusing to shake his hand.

During the medical questioning, it became clear that Marie was inappropriately interested in her daughter's behind. She was constantly inspecting it and exploring her anus with her finger. She was asked to ignore the problem and to no longer touch this part of her daughter's body. Melanie and her mother were also sent to see a child psychiatrist. The latter only saw them once and concluded, succinctly, that the little girl's encopresis took up all the family's emotional space, in particular her mother's. Nevertheless, these two appointments completely resolved the problem of anal incontinence.

At this point, Melanie's father entered the scene. He joined his wife and daughter for a couple of appointments. He held their little boy on his knees and applauded the fact that the boy had fewer problems than his daughter. He even congratulated the doctor for the surprising and rapid results. On the other hand, the mother did not share the enthusiasm for the nearly magical disappearance of anal incontinence, but bitterly complained that her daughter got angry more often now and said "no." The family then rejected the clinician, making it clear the mother wore the pants in this family and nobody showed up for any of the next four appointments made for Melanie and her parents.

Two and a half years went by without any consultation. Then Marie took her daughter to see a gastroenterologist in the same hospital. She complained that Melanie had been psychologically traumatized by the previous clinician. The second doctor took note of the fact that anal incontinence had disappeared immediately after the appointment with his colleague. Two years later, it had still not reappeared. As it was obvious from the family's behavior that any attempt to suggest a psychological problem would be poorly received, the doctor made no mention of it. He therefore managed rather easily to do tests and make a functional evaluation of Melanie's constipation.

The problem was located only in the left side of the large intestine. The right colon functioned normally. Limited stase in the left colon and the rectum is very characteristic of Irritable Bowel Syndrome. One week after Melanie had swallowed twenty radiopaque markers visible on x-rays, she hadn't defecated any of them. Her constipation was therefore very severe, and reproducible. Melanie also had anismus.

The gastroenterologist decided to prescribe biofeedback work on Melanie's perineum, giving strict instructions not to imply any psychological interpretation. In addition, he had a man conduct the reeducation, rather than the woman who usually did it. Melanie's anismus was corrected at the first session, but it returned at the second and persisted.

The gastroenterologist saw the mother and daughter eight times. Discouraged by this family, he also decided to send them to a child psychiatrist. The mother didn't keep this appointment either nor did they come back to see the doctor. Instead she changed gastroenterologists. The third clinician, still in the same hospital, reviewed the whole history. He decided to send Melanie to the technician working with the surgeon who had seen her first, and after the second appointment, he transferred the child back to this surgeon.

The mother and daughter then reappeared eight years after their first appointment. Melanie had grown quite a bit and had become slim. She now had long hair down to her shoulders. She was performing remarkably well in school. But her face held great sadness, and she only responded to questions with gestures. When we told her she looked sad, she immediately started to sob. Her mother monopolized the conversation, revealing that she herself regularly had diarrhea.

Melanie's constipation had not changed. She could go twenty days without a bowel movement and ended up regularly at the emergency room to have evacuating enemas. This time, they kept their appointments on a more regular basis. At the beginning, Melanie began to say "no" to her mother, who became just as furious about this negativism as before. Without too much trouble, the father took over so that the doctors could run various examinations. As foreseen, Melanie's rectum was huge and insensitive, with persisting anismus.

During this period, the teenager's dentist sent her to see a speech therapist. The speech therapist observed her pushing her tongue out of her mouth and contracting her lips. He diagnosed Melanie with infantile or atypical swallowing. Melanie and her mother cancelled four of the nine appointments aimed at treating this problem. The teenager did not do her exercises regularly. A psychological consultation was recommended to the family, who again refused. Frustrated, the speech therapist stopped seeing the mother and daughter. In his records, he recorded a diagnosis of non-compliance, a term used to describe disobedient patients who only do what they want to do.

During one of the biofeedback sessions with the female technician, Marie, Melanie's mother, finally confided that between the ages of eight and sixteen she had been repeatedly sexually abused by her stepfather, who fondled her breasts, vulva and anus. Following this revelation, Marie decided that she would have her own digestive problems treated. It ended up just as difficult to treat her as it had been her daughter. Marie missed appointments, refused consultations and any discussions not limited exclusively to her intestines.

Marie's history was typical of Irritable Bowel Syndrome, oscillating between two bowel movements in a day to one every second day. As soon as she experienced stress, her stools turned liquid. At the age of thirty-three, she had a hysterectomy because her periods were too abundant. Of course, her uterus was normal, as is always the case among abused women. Marie declared that she had an excellent relationship with her husband, without any sexual problems. She did not feel abdominal pain during penetration, nor during or after coitus. Their sexual encounters lasted over a half an hour. She had orgasms from caresses and from penetration, but they only had sex once a month.

The technician shared Marie's secret of abuse with the clinician, who said nothing to Marie. Marie waited a year and a half before confiding in him. Her elder sister had not been abused by their stepfather, but the younger one had. Nothing had happened to the youngest girl, who was the daughter of Marie's mother and her stepfather. Marie complained to her mother about the abuse, but she did not believe her.

As soon as Marie reached the age of sixteen, she left the family. "When I was pregnant with Melanie," she said, "and I was still in my pajamas in the morning, and I knew that my stepfather was coming over, I ran to get dressed because I was so afraid that he was going to harass me again. I can never forgive him for what he did to Melanie."

The stepfather was also physically violent with Marie's older sister. She also said that her grandmother was sometimes extremely nice and, at other times, very mean. In fact, when she said the word "grandmother," Marie meant her own mother, mixing up Melanie with herself, transgressing the generational layers, which is called "telescoping generations."

We suggested that she write down everything that went through her head, particularly the things linked to abuse.

Thanks to the work of J.W. Pennebaker and his colleagues, we know that the revelation of family secrets has an extremely positive impact on the immune system and lowers the number of subsequent illnesses. Marie read her text aloud in Melanie's presence. The two women cried for a long time in each other's arms.

Marie's grandmother had also been very violent physically and her mother had also left her dysfunctional home at the age of sixteen. At barely eighteen, she already had three children. Marie's father left her mother when her mother was pregnant with her. Marie was then sexually abused by her stepfather and very often beaten physically. She still had scars, which were visible on her legs, indelible marks of where her mother and stepfather had beaten her.

During this period, Melanie started talking a little. She stuttered a lot. From time to time she had a spontaneous bowel movement, without the help of laxatives or enemas. Then we learned that her grandmother also had defecation problems. And other revelations were to follow: her cousin, the daughter of her mother's eldest sister had been abused with death threats. She too had very hard time defecating.

Melanie has not recovered, even though her mother voiced her story. But the story goes on, and Marie and her daughter continue to help each other try to unwind this vicious tangle.

A Spectacular Case Of Anniversary Syndrome

We told Miriam's story in detail in another book (*Ce que les maux de ventre disent de notre passé*), but it is so spectacular and so far from rational that we would like to come back to it (Devroede, 2002). To sum the case up, a teenager was delivering newspapers one winter evening and had an accident. She was sliding down snow banks between two deliveries. On one, she couldn't stop, slid beyond the bank, fell and impaled herself vaginally on a metal bar that was marking the road. It was a miracle she survived. She had emergency surgery. The only damage caused by the metal bar, which perforated the hymen and ran right through to the thorax, was two little holes in one part of the intestine, near the stomach.

The young girl didn't even spend two weeks in the hospital. Most of the damage caused by the accident was psychological. Miriam was twelve years old. The work on post-traumatic stress revealed that her mother, her grandmother and her great-grandmother had all been raped at the age of… twelve!

This story is unexpected when compared with the others we have recounted. In the others, you can draw a relational continuity between the victim of sexual abuse and victim's offspring. You also find a process similar to the repetition compulsion, so important to psychoanalysts.

Despite its traumatic and morbid nature, this compulsion carries in it an instinct to live, an internal healing process. The subject progresses, even in small steps, until he learns what he is looking for through that repetition.

Let's go back to Miriam. The family dynamics changed quite a bit during the follow-up on these multi-generational traumas. The teenager said that her parents were constantly fighting and that her mother wanted to leave her father. She also talked a lot about their sexuality, because her mother had told her she had never experienced sexual pleasure. Her parents had not made love in eight years. Miriam added that she had never seen her parents kiss or show any sign of tenderness.

Miriam and her parents refused to see a child psychiatrist to help them process their past. The young girl started having nightmares and, for the first time in her life, began to remember her dreams. In these nightmares, she was drawing a picture of her mother in the process of killing her eldest brother, who was then seventeen.

Miriam also expressed her anger towards this brother, who had abused her when she was only four. He had given her money, and threatened her with physical violence and blackmail if she were to say anything. He was not very old at the time: he was only eight when he abused her, using coercion to touch her anus and vulva, and forcing her to do the same with his penis.

She remembered that she already had moments of dissociation at the time, because she recalled when he came into her room, she woke up in her bed without any recollection of what happened in the mean time. Again, she refused to see a child psychiatrist. During this period, her schoolwork improved considerably.

Miriam became depressed and starting leaving letters begging for help. This finally led her mother to accept seeing a child psychiatrist, who treated Miriam for nearly a year. During this time, Miriam became aware that the accident had distanced her from her mother, breaking up what had previously been a very close relationship, one that had been open, happy, and symbiotic. She also realized that, on the contrary, this distance had improved her relationship with her father, who was virtually absent before that.

The themes discussed with the therapist revolved around feminine identity and the absence of a male role model. Miriam also worked on the transfer that occurred with the surgeon who had saved her life. She had a brief period of anorexia that lasted a few months. She said that the accident had helped her to get closer to people, to tell them that she loved them, but that it had also forced her to grow up prematurely.

She managed to overcome the anorexia, remaining fearful of having a love relationship for a period of time, since she was afraid of being abandoned. She started using boys only to prove to herself that she was still likable, despite the accident.

Two years later, she was in perfect health. She had blossomed and become a very beautiful young woman. Her parents still lived together. She thought they would be better off separated, but it was not her place to get involved in their problems. She had a new boyfriend. She experienced orgasm from caresses and from penetration. She was at the top of her class, acted in a play, and had received an acting award. She finally went for it and made a career for herself.

Miriam's story is a fine example of what we are trying to

illustrate in this book. Clearly, the family's secret was undermining the teenager's future.

The traumatism could have been of another nature than that of sexual abuse repeated from mother to daughter, and that is the essential message we want to get across. Sexual abuse is only one of many cases of a strong person abusing authority over a weaker one, an adult over a child, a man over a woman, etc. Moreover, both the abusers and the abused tend to greatly confuse male and female identity.

A healing process had already been set into motion with Miriam's mother, because Miriam had not yet been truly abused when she accidentally impaled herself. We cannot reasonably refer to abuse between a brother and sister of the same age, although the little boy had forced her, and the family path was signposted towards rape.

Naming things, casting raw light on closeted secrets has certainly been difficult for this family. As a result, all the family members have been forced to change. But one can reasonably hope that at the end of the path, once the necessary grieving of past pain has been completed, all the protagonists will have the chance to live a happy life.

The stories told in this chapter all recount children who have benefited from a certain amount of help from their parents, a certain questioning on the part of their parents.

Unfortunately, that is not always possible. It cannot occur when the parents are deceased, or too old or physically rundown to affront the intensity of the storms that occur in the body when emotions repressed an entire lifetime come to the surface. Children grow up.

When children have been abused, once they become adult, how do they manage to live through the impact of traumas of a sexual nature or not? When are they relatively free from their parents, even though they are still unable to count on them in the healing process?

This is what we will explore in the following chapter, which looks into a further, more complex step in the process of healing our parents' trauma.

Chapter III

When Parents are Obstacles to Recovery

Becoming Adult

A little boy cried in his stepmother's arms. She cradled him lovingly. "When I am with my mother, I miss my father, and when I am with my father, I miss my mother," he sobbed.

Countless are the children beaten, neglected, abandoned or adopted, still with their parents who are tearing each other apart, or parents now divorced or widowed. Frequently these children find themselves in the situation of having to help and console the parent who remains, to heal that parent's wounds—without doing it on purpose. It could be a mother left alone, but also more and more frequently an abandoned father. Literally, the child ends up replacing the missing parent.

In Canada, income tax forms have legalized this incestuous marital situation by describing these children as "spouse-equivalents", children who father or mother their parents. This process, which is called parentification, is at least as difficult for them to handle as the abandonment they have experienced. Psychoanalyst Didier Dumas (1999) discusses the consequences of missing father figures in his work *Sans Père, Sans Parole* (No Fathers, No Words), while Guy Corneau (1989) talks about "absent fathers, lost sons" (Dumas, 1999; Corneau, 1989). But girls are also lost due to these tragedies, even if they are more isolated than boys and quicker able to manage alone in life.

So many couples separate when a birth occurs! It is perhaps simplistic, but true, to say that the father loses his position of "pseudo-baby," being replaced by a real one. More than half of the fathers in Quebec experience what is commonly known as the Couvade Syndrome, which means they fall ill after the birth of a child, the most frequent affliction being toothaches.

During the Middle Ages, the "couvade" was a custom where the father took to his bed at the time of birth to present his baby, while the mother quickly hurried to return to work in the fields, thus certainly avoiding a lot of phlebitis—blood clots in leg veins—and the deadly embolisms that occur when those clots migrate to the lungs.

It's hard to know which is worse, Charybdis or Scylla (Lattimore, 1967/1906)? Is an unhappy marriage better than a divorce where the two parents remain loving parents to their children? Even under the worst living and survival conditions, some children turn out well, even very well, and reconstruct a life that is nearly normal, even if that life is based on a weak foundation at whose mercy they will always be.

In one way, in their unhappiness, today's children are lucky, because they often have the opportunity to benefit from the misfortune of their parents' divorce. The symptom of divorce, which is spreading more and more as if it were a contagious disease, probably symbolizes new demands between spouses, the beginning of the awareness that one cannot raise inner awareness for the other, and that seeking happiness outside of oneself is nothing more than an illusion.

This illusion has caused a lot of suffering in children whose unhappy parents stay together for their own good. Children also suffer a lot when the illusion shatters. A recent survey of a thousand French people showed that progress had been made in the quality of the relationship between parents and children and that a distantiation or differentiation factor, which is essential for becoming a mature adult, has been at work for a century.

All children want to heal their parents, and they can indeed contribute to their parents' recovery. In Western societies, where more than half the couples end up divorced, children have learned to look upon the difficult passage faced by their parents with distance, to be detached from it. They have learned what their elders didn't know: to look at their parents with adult eyes rather than with childlike credibility, even at a more advanced age.

Certainly, it is ideal for a child to be raised and loved by his biologic parents. In this way, there is continuity between coming into this world and later taking one's freedom and living a separate life. There is less risk of frustration and accumulated loss. The work surrounding a successful divorce is the work of bereavement. And divorce is successful when the two partners manage to detail the unconscious reasons for which their marriage did not last. This clarification has positive effects on their kids.

We have seen that a parent who has been sexually abused

and who manages to voice the trauma that was experienced does not turn that trauma into a family secret and therefore allows his or her child to benefit from this questioning and the dialogue that is established with his or her descendents.

In all cases, children are like sponges. They absorb everything that is in their environment, showing it in their bodies if secrets are not named. In the same way, when a parent enters a healing process, he or she best bring the children along. Then the entire family dynamic finds itself transformed.

As a result, pediatricians are more and more frequently adopting a systemic family approach, where not only the child is treated, but the family. However, what happens when a child is born into a family where the women, raped from mother to daughter, are subject to a repetitive pattern over several generations without ever calling that pattern into question?

Unquestioning Parents

Angela was thirty-nine years old. She complained that for the past four years she had suffered from constant, severe, chronic and painful constipation. Prior to this, she had had a long history of chronic diarrhea dating back to her infancy. When she was thirty, she left her homeland of Canada to live in France. As soon as she got there, she sought out a therapist, whom she saw with her husband.

Angela spontaneously went into great detail about a horribly difficult childhood. There were two girls and six boys in her family. The two girls had been sexually abused by the same brother. Her sister, who was four years older, had been subject to full vaginal penetration on several occasions. She died of a heart attack at the age of forty. Angela had also been abused a lot, starting at the age of seven. In fact, she had no childhood memories prior to that age, which always indicates that the familial environment was inadequate.

She frequently wet her bed throughout her childhood. As soon as she became a teenager, she had an intense sex life. She had a lot of sadomasochistic fantasies and loved being sodomized. Spontaneously, she started talking about the incest her mother, grandmother and great grandmother had been victims of in the Quebec countryside. Angela remembered how much she hated what she felt as a child when her mother took her temperature using a rectal thermometer. Her mother followed her to France as soon as her alcoholic husband died.

It was extremely easy to communicate with Angela. It was even disconcerting, as questions were so superfluous. It was more of a monologue than a dialogue. The consultation lasted ninety minutes, much longer than the national standard of fifteen minutes. We decided to work on evaluating the constipation and the abdominal pain. As a dissociation tool, in Ericksonian hypnosis terms, we suggested she produce two drawings of herself, one showing her suffering from abdominal pain, and the other without pain.

She was given a first appointment to have a proctoscopy simply to evaluate the anal muscle tone and reflexes. The doctor would use a rigid instrument, requiring no laxatives or enemas. But Angela did not show up for the appointment. One hour before the set time, she sent the two drawings by fax. The fax read, "This fax replaces my proctoscopy appointment. Dear doctor, hello. I am sure that life meant for us to cross paths. This meeting was decisive for me, and I wanted to share the following with you. I recovered when we met! I think that you finally allowed me to finish my incest therapy. I worked on the question a lot with my therapists. I made a ton of connections between my sexuality, first as a child then as an adult, and my large intestine's behavior. I think I understood that I carried my mother's ancestral shame and fear in my belly. You reassured me by supplying me with factual information. It's as if miracles happen in your office, but I think that it is all the result of a long process begun when I left Canada, a process that has led me to a deep inner peace. I would really appreciate it if you were to call me at my appointment time. Angela."

Her drawings were very simple. The one where she had a stomachache represented a stick figure with a spiral on his belly, very similar to what Françoise Dolto describes as the confused ideas a child can have about male-female identity and the path from desire to conception (Dolto, 1969, 1984, 1988, 1993). The drawing of her without a stomachache was different. She had noted the difference herself on the drawing: she had hair. And this time she was wearing a dress.

We called Angela at the exact time she was to have had the proctoscopy. She asked if it was still necessary to undergo the prescribed tests. As she no longer had any symptoms, her tests were, of course, cancelled. She asked if she could take leave; she never returned. She had plans to take a year off to sail around the world with her husband and children.

Jeanne's Story

When a long-suffering parent's silence is guarded for a long time, recovery is much more difficult. This is what happened to Jeanne.

At the age of twenty-five, she consulted us for a problem of extremely severe constipation. She only had bowel movements every one or two months! All medical attempts to help her had failed. Her doctor sent her to see us, over a thousand miles from where she lived. Jeanne wasn't lying. Over a period of two weeks, she did not defecate any of the radiopaque markers we had given her to ingest to measure transit time. Transit took much longer than it normally does both in the right and the left parts of the large intestine. These tests were repeated and continued to give abnormal results. Jeanne also suffered from anismus.

When she was asked to strain, as if to defecate, she tightened her anus when straining forcefully. She also had rectal insensitivity, as she felt nothing until a balloon was filled with two hundred milliliters of water. The normal maximum volume tolerated is only two hundred and sixty milliliters. She therefore also had a problem of rectal insensitivity.

Jeanne was not very inclined to questioning herself and was therefore not a good candidate to be sent to a psychiatrist or a psychologist to speak a whole lot about her life. We decided to help her by trying to correct the anismus with biofeedback, without asking too many questions.

We also asked her to participate in a research trial for new medication for Irritable Bowel Syndrome with constipation.

She probably received the active medication rather than the inactive placebo, because very soon thereafter she started have bowel movements every three or four days, and this lasted for a period of two years. When the medication trial was over, her stubborn constipation came back as strong as ever.

Throughout this process, Jeanne nevertheless began to talk about her past, recounting a long story about her complicated love life. She talked about how she had been a victim of sexual abuse when she was seven years old. Her babysitter, a young sixteen-year-old man, forced her to perform fellatio. Her elder brother had also abused her sexually. He started to talk to her about it because he too had been abused. Together they dug up old memories of an unknown man and woman who had been present during the sexual abuse but neither of them remembered any details about them.

Jeanne remembered that she had abdominal pain constantly when she was little during the period of the abuse and that her father often brought her to the emergency room. She only mentioned her parents' divorce three years after her first appointment. During the period of revelations, she had an intense emotional reaction every time she defecated and afterwards, she felt completely empty, both literally and figuratively.

Jeanne was abused again, as was the same brother, when she reached the age of nine, by a cousin who touched her vulva with his penis, but spared her penetration. She had two younger brothers, and she said that when she was little, she tried very hard to behave like a boy, because she realized that her mother preferred her three sons. Of course, she felt much closer to her father.

Jeanne was only seventeen when she gave birth to her first child, a daughter. Just before she came to consult for herself, she learned that her daughter had been abused at the age of four, without Jeanne even being aware of it. She also learned that her daughter was suicidal. She forced her daughter's abuser to get psychological help.

At the age of nineteen, Jeanne had a second daughter with another man. When she talked about this daughter, she made grammatical mistakes, designating her with the masculine form "him or his". Her third child was—finally—a boy, by yet another man. As soon as she gave birth to this son, she became orgasmic to caresses and to penetration.

She also started having intense abdominal pain during and after sex, a common symptom among people with Irritable Bowel Syndrome. She felt pain upon penetration, but that did not keep her from orgasm. Sexual intercourse began to provoke memories of abuse and, after having made love, she started feeling the same inner emptiness she felt after defecation.

Jeanne evolved a lot in therapy. She cut her long blond hair very short, like a tomboy. She began to express the hate she felt towards all of the men in her life to this point. Nevertheless, in addition to the relationship she had with her little boy's father, she entered into one with another man with whom she had intense orgasms.

For the first time in her life, she became capable of sharing tenderness with a man and even let him kiss her, something she had never allowed with previous lovers. Her son's father, on the other hand, became violent with her and she had to seek police protection. She moved to another city to flee him.

One day, Jeanne brought her young boy in. He had been constipated since birth. And he will probably remain so as long as his mother has not recovered from her own childhood. Now Jeanne wants to recover to help Jerome.

Three Strikes

When a parent with a history of abuse has suffered too much to be able to start processing the past, his or her child continues to bear the weight of his ancestor's pain. One wonders if a surrogate parental figure could perhaps help the child become an adult to free himself from his ancestor's suffering. This is the case of Anouk.

Anouk was given her name almost as a reverse image, as her sister bore the surprising name of Kouna, the two names being the backward spelling of one another. Anouk had a spectacular start in life: she was conceived and began developing around an IUD in her mother's womb. Consequently, she felt rejected and unwanted as a child. She was constipated from birth. As a child, her gigantic stools often blocked up the toilets. When she consulted doctors for her problem at the age of twenty-six, she was only having bowel movements once every three weeks. She had abdominal pain after sexual intercourse, and it was easy to diagnose her with Irritable Bowel Syndrome.

During the examination of her anorectal region, her anus was extremely tight, proof that she had anismus. When we asked her to tighten the anus, she barely moved her anal sphincter, but violently tightened her buttocks, squeezing together her thighs and feet and rocking her pelvis onto the finger doing the rectal examination, a little bit as if she was having sexual intercourse. Clearly, her awareness of this part of her body was very defective.

Anouk came to the second appointment accompanied by her mother who confided in us in the hallway afterwards that her daughter HAD been abused by her stepfather starting at the age of five and up until her marriage. She had been subject to full penetration at the age of sixteen. Her mother was aware of the abuse. She also said, with regards to Anouk: "She and I are the same person." Anouk never returned after her mother confided this information, which was so important for the future of her daughter.

The story of Sandra also demonstrates what happens when a mother's suffering from sexual abuse is too great for her to talk about. Her experience must be shared to liberate her child, who carries it in his or her body.

First of all, Sandra was wrongly operated on for appendicitis, the organ being normal when observed under a microscope by a pathologist. She suffered from persistent, painful constipation. A particularly intense crisis was wrongly diagnosed, leading to the operation. Sandra had been constipated since birth and had a son in the same situation. Sandra had bowel movements twice a week and was diagnosed with Irritable Bowel Syndrome.

Her husband was thirty years older than she was. She felt pain upon penetration and in her belly during and after sexual intercourse. Occasionally, she had orgasms from caresses and from penetration.

For the first time in her life, she revealed that she had been raped at the age of seven by her step-father, who forced her repeatedly to have oral, anal and genital relations with him until she was fourteen. She had also been abused by an older brother and by a cousin. In addition, she had more recently been raped by someone she said was a "friend." This time she took action starting legal proceedings. Her husband, in guise of support, said she had asked for it.

Her colonoscopy was normal, except for the presence of numerous spasms in the colon. The digital rectal exam caused the same abdominal pain she experienced during sexual intercourse, and Sandra suffered from severe anismus.

She expressed explicitly that she was incapable of cutting the bond she had with her son. She still breastfed him at the age of four. Sandra and her little boy remain to this day fusional and constipated, although she did stop breastfeeding.

Sometimes, the anguish that follows revelation overwhelms the person who has the revelation and causes them to flee until they are able to integrate its impact. This was probably the case with Frances. She was thirty-seven years old when she came to consult with us for a problem of constipation since birth. She never waited more than a week before taking laxatives, but had no memories of ever having had a spontaneous bowel movement without taking medication. In addition, after divorcing her first husband, she developed severe, cramp-like abdominal pain.

Without us asking any questions, she spontaneously began to verbalize many details concerning her terrible childhood and a classic pattern of re-victimization. Her maternal grandfather was a pedophile. He abused all his daughters, including Frances's mother. As a child, Frances had a very poor relationship with her mother, who beat her a lot. On the other hand, she said she had had a remarkably good relationship with her father, who had not abused her either physically or sexually. He had died twenty years earlier. She was still crying over his premature death from a stroke at the age of forty-seven.

Her grandfather had repeatedly touched her sexually. She had talked to her mother about it, but the latter did not believe her. Then, her eldest brother, who was then seventeen, raped her three times. Again, her mother did not believe her. At the age of sixteen, she was raped by someone she didn't know, whom her mother forced her to wed when she was three months pregnant. Her husband abused her physically and sexually, forcing sodomy and constantly telling her that her stool was sickening. She became terrified to defecate.

Afterwards, she had a second husband for fourteen years. This one did not abuse her physically or sexually, but she said he was very cruel mentally. During this relationship, they were both frequently suicidal, without ever acting on it.

Her third husband, the one she had now, was extremely kind and understanding. There was no violence between them, nor was there any sexual desire. In fact, they had no sexual relationship. It was as if her happiness made her sick; the pain she felt upon penetration was so intense, her husband couldn't even get close to her.

Of her four brothers, one died in a car accident, another committed suicide at the age of fifteen, a third died of prostate cancer, and she had cut off contact with the fourth, the one who had abused her.

As usual, we prescribed tests. The patient never showed up for the endoscopy, her first appointment. We had also recommended that she see a urologist for an associated problem of urinary incontinence. She never showed up for the cystoscopy either, to examine the bladder. One day, she showed up at the emergency room with severe lower back pain. She was registered for admission, but when she was called to see the doctor, she had disappeared.

The Miracle Of A Loving Mother

A good mother who questions herself and tries to free herself of a personal problem for the love of her daughter sometimes ranks as a small miracle. This is the case of Anne and her daughter Marianne.

Anne was seen for the first time when she was three. She became constipated at the time of toilet training. She had had no problem with defecation prior to the age of two. Afterwards, she had bowel movements once a week, with hard, infrequent stools. When she finally told her parents, she had not had a bowel movement in a month. Laxatives and enemas were totally useless. Her father was also constipated, having a bowel movement only once every two weeks. Her mother described in great detail the efforts her daughter had to make to defecate. She used anatomical precision when she described the anus opening and the stool remaining behind it, incapable of coming out.

An anorectal manometry was performed. There was no

rectoanal inhibitory reflex, the physiological reflex we have already mentioned. She was therefore diagnosed as having Hirschsprung's Disease. A child psychiatrist, finding the relationship between the mother and the daughter to be profoundly troubled, recommended waiting. Yet despite this opinion, the child was operated on. There were no nerve cells in the specimen, and the child started having a bowel movement every day right after the operation. The diagnosis of the Hirschsprung's Disease was thus confirmed. Anne did not return to the hospital for twenty-five years.

She came back four months after the birth of her first child, a little girl whom she had named Marianne, clearly echoing her own name. Anne once again complained of constipation, and she had blood in her stools, which is always a worrying clinical sign. She said she had had relatively minor problems of constipation during her pregnancy, which then disappeared until she gave birth. Once she delivered, she became persistently constipated. Her little girl was constipated too.

Her entire record was reviewed, including the information available from twenty-five years ago, when anismus was unknown. We concluded that at that time she had probably suffered from anismus, which hid the rectoanal inhibitory reflex and led to an erroneous diagnosis of Hirschsprung's Disease. Her constipation was analyzed in the regular manner, which showed nothing more than Irritable Bowel Syndrome.

During a visit with her mother and her daughter, Anne made a revelation she had never made to her mother. When she was five, her older sister, age nine, had forced cunnilingus upon her. The experience could have been nothing more than a game of discovery, except she experienced it traumatically. That sister's identity seemed a bit unclear. Her ex-husband had been bisexual during their marriage, becoming homosexual afterwards.

As soon as Anne spoke about what she had experienced as abuse, the little Marianne instantly recovered from her constipation. Her intestinal disorders ceased, and she never experienced the symptoms again. Anne also recovered and began thinking about her family history. One day, she admitted that on more than one occasion, she had had the perverse impulsion to perform cunnilingus on her baby. She later noticed that her daughter had experienced very severe constipation on the days when she had had these perverse thoughts.

It turned out that there had been a lot of alcoholism and sexual violence on her mother's side of the family. Anne was very close to her maternal grandmother who, after spending her life constipated, died of cancer at the age of ninety-four. Anne described the old lady as somebody totally dissociated, both kind and cruel. Anne helped her to have a peaceful death. We also learned that her father's mother had a history of sexual abuse.

Today, Anne and Marianne are in fine health.

Chapter IV

Symbolic Abuse

Susan

Susan was raped by her father at the age of sixteen, and her mother never knew it. It was anal rape. She had been profoundly hurt by the fact that her little sister, who shared the same bed, had turned her back, hiding under the covers in order not to see or hear anything. At that time, Susan did not know that her father regularly raped all five of his daughters.

She was constipated, very constipated. She had a bowel movement once every two months! Her problem was so severe and so unresponsive to treatment that there had been some talk of removing her large intestine. She was incapable of expelling the enemas administered. She did not respond to suppositories. Laxatives didn't work.

She was often hospitalized and, with intense pain, made enormous efforts to unblock herself. She suddenly recovered from her stubborn constipation after her father died and she placed a long letter in his casket in which she vented all the accumulated emotion she had held against him.

For a few years, her intestines continued to behave normally. Then when her husband began to have mistresses, she passed to the extreme opposite, with intense diarrhea and about thirty liquid stools a day. There too, it was a functional problem, without any possible surgical or medical treatment.

Her husband ended up leaving her. She took a more or less asexual lover. After a year, he managed to make love to her. Her diarrhea stopped when she turned him out.

Susan very slowly discovered sensuality and sexuality. At the age of fifty-five, she was able to experience orgasm with a man for the first time in her life, and even several orgasms during penetration. She nevertheless continued to have a fragile digestive system, and whenever some crisis occurred, whatever its nature, she had diarrhea.

This had just happened. Her diarrhea had been caused by the fact that Susan had discovered her lover making love to an old woman, one twenty years older than he was. In addition to the diarrhea, Susan complained of having seen traces of light red blood in her stools. The symptom was alarming enough to look further than the chronic diagnosis of functional digestive disorders. We decided to examine the large intestine with a colonoscopy. Susan's reaction was awful. During the examination, she did not move and did not complain of any pain. But right after the instrument had been removed from her anus; she started hyperventilating and had a very intense fit of hysterics. Normally, she did not cry or scream. But on this occasion, she cried out in a totally inappropriate manner. The fit continued, getting worse after the examination. It was only after she had calmed down that it became possible for her to express in words what she had experienced. Susan found herself in a context sufficiently safe for her to feel authorized to relive all that she had felt when she had been violently sodomized by her father at the age of sixteen.

Intrusive Medical Treatment

Invading another's body be it through the person's natural orifices or through a physical penetration by needles or surgical incisions carries with it a sexual and phallic dimension. All depends on the caregiver's attitude. That being said, it has been shown that sexually abused subjects undergo more surgery compared with others. There probably exist perverse and totally unconscious mechanisms that explain this behavior. There is also a process of healing at work, such as the victim's unconscious quest to recover through having yet another wound. Psychoanalysts speak about a repetition compulsion.

All orifices are concerned: mouth, anus, vulva, urinary meatus, ears, nose and eyes. It is not surprising then that it is often in the units where endoscopies are performed to explore the lower digestive tube that patients experience very intense reactions that result in silenced stories of sexual abuse resurfacing, as was the case with Susan.

"I saw your little protégé today to do a barium enema," a radiologist recounted to me. "He was an extremely difficult one, completely agitated on the examination table. I had to get angry with him and use my authority to put in the enema cannula to manage to perform a decent test. He was really troublesome."

Too bad, I thought, because later I found out that the teenager in question had been sodomized several times by his eldest brother. At the time of the examination, we were simply exploring a problem of stubborn constipation. He was in a foster home. His parents had had their parental custody removed. They had two children: the abuser and the abused. The first son was the mother's pet. The father preferred the second son. But the father was dominated by the mother, and she let her favorite son abuse the younger son. The radiologist could have shown a little more sensitivity during the test.

Suppositories, Thermometers And Enemas

Why are Europeans more willing to use suppositories than North Americans? The same question applies to taking the temperature: through the rectum, under the arm or under the tongue. It all depends on the culture. We could certainly evoke Protestant Puritanism, which is so prevalent in North America. The fact remains that there is nothing rational about using the rectum to administer medication for use by the entire body.

Experiments have been carried out to see where suppositories meant to treat the rectoanal region end up. When they are imbibed with gastrografin, a contrast agent used for localizing them, it is surprising to note that due to the backwards motor activity of the large intestine, the suppositories climb up just under the spleen and the liver. It is therefore not logical, scientifically speaking, to treat a rectoanal pathology with suppositories.

With regards to medication, the general idea is that suppositories are less harmful because the rectum has no gustatory papilla like the stomach. Therefore, there is no risk of indigestion. Yet numerous people have traumatic memories linked to the insertion of suppositories, thermometers and enemas during their infancy.

Sylvia, for example, who had been sexually abused repeatedly when she was little, had been operated on several times, uselessly, for pain so severe it impressed her doctors. In these crisis situations, avoidable operations often occur due to the dramatic nature of the clinical presentation and the insistence among some patients to have surgery that is supposed to resolve their problems. Exploratory laparotomy is where the abdomen is opened with a large cut. In diagnostic laparoscopy, the holes are a little smaller and less painful, but it is still an aggression. Appendectomy: oops!

Often the appendix shows up normal when examined under a microscope after surgery. Sometimes a normal uterus is removed under the pretext of painful or too abundant menstruation. At other times, simple divertucula are accused of causing diverticulitis, which after an in-depth medical evaluation proves not to be the case, meaning that the problem was simply colic spasms often associated with diverticulosis, of which they are often a precursor.

Sylvia complained of difficulty expulsing her stools. She had anismus, as is frequently the case of women who have been victims of rape. She found a way to replace her father. She found a treatment that both prolonged the paternal penetrations and relieved the difficulties she had in defecating. To have bowel movements, she frenetically used suppositories, three times a day. For a year, she no longer tried to have any further surgery. She spoke a lot about her childhood and the family dysfunctions that preceded the period during which she was abused.

During this year when she spoke about the abuse, Sylvia continued to ritually insert a suppository three times a day. She needed this entire talking time, a period of distancing herself from her parents, her family and her surroundings, in order to begin to realize the symbolism of this "therapeutic" daily anal penetration. And even so, her growing awareness only took the form of a question:

> "Do you think doctor that one of the reasons for which only suppositories work?"
> "Of course not."
> "What do you mean?"
> "Have you thought of the symbolism of these suppositories?"

Sylvia then became extremely angry with the doctor who had allowed her to masturbate her anus three times a day, thus prolonging her childhood abuse. She stopped immediately and never used suppositories again. Today, she is a therapist and organizes a support group for abused women. Since she was abused herself, she is extraordinarily efficient.

Good Old TV!

Symbolism is sometimes more traumatizing. This is the case with Diane. When she was little, her father often took her down into the basement, where he whipped her before sodomizing her. Her mother was upstairs in the kitchen. Later, Diane was abused by her step-brother. When she consulted us, she had rectal prolapse. The rectum protruded through the anus, as if she had a penis between her legs. This analogy was made by another patient who had also been abused by her father and who constantly spoke about her own complete rectal prolapse as being her "penis."

At the time, Diane was the mistress of the town priest. Their sexuality was sadly shallow. He dragged her into the countryside where, full of guilt, he made love to her expediently. However, he did visit her when she was in the hospital. Once the rectum had been sutured in place inside the pelvis, onto the sacrum, a control test revealed whitish patches on the rectal mucusa. She was first diagnosed with rectal leukoplakia, a disorder of the mucus membranes in the rectum, which are normally red but become all white, like the skin. This diagnosis suggests a risk of developing rectal cancer. The diagnosis was erroneous.

It took a lot of time, a lot of developing trust, for the patient to admit that she regularly, violently masturbated her anus and rectum. She had caused her own wounds. Scar tissue in the rectum looked like leukoplakia. Diane revealed—showing how much she had been dramatically traumatized by her family—that she masturbated her anus and only managed to have an orgasm while watching the news on television.

A psychoanalyst once said that all television images are a sublimation of the primitive scene, when a child witnessed sexual relations between parents by surprise, for the first time. Diane's case is the only one we know of that illustrates this premise. In a certain way, her anal masturbation symbolically represented abuse, because the patient's finger took the place of her father's penis when she was little.

When Toilet Training Goes Wrong

During toilet training, there are opportunities for things to take a wrong symbolic tangent related to sexuality. We know that during toilet training, parents introduce an element of heterosexuality. A mother can be more ill at ease with her son, a father with his daughter. Yet, toilet training is not about genital or sexual functions, but simply about urination and defecation.

Some mothers and fathers find some pleasure in carrying out anal intromissions on their child. For a good cause, they think. But do they know what their children are feeling? During a psychodrama workshop, a nurse revealed that when she was little, she had always felt uneasy when her mother inserted a suppository. When she opened this door, one inferring the possibility of sexual abuse, she was led to speak for four full hours about the relationship she had with her mother, then with her father. The suppositories were only a small element in this very inadequate relationship.

Non-sexual Abuse

Under certain circumstances, sexuality *seems* to be completely absent from certain behavioral patterns.

A man was getting ready to have an exercise electrocardiogram to know whether he could safely take a scuba diving course. He showed up at the lab. The technician asked him to remove his shirt. The patient asked him why. The technician explained he had to stick electrodes onto different places on his thorax in order to test him while he walked on the treadmill. To his great surprise, the patient saw the technician approaching his thorax holding in his hand an electrical instrument with a revolving stem, vaguely resembling a screwdriver.

Still not relaxed, he asked the technician about this instrument. Blandly, the technician responded that it is necessary to scratch the skin a little bit so that it did not lose contact with the electrodes when he sweated, thus keeping an electrical contact with the blood.

An immediate outburst occurred. This patient was used to self-hypnotic induction. He disassociated, as abused children often do. He entered a trance, without having felt any pain, with the first superficial incision. Later, he said he had observed the scene as if he had been separated from his body. He had seen the serosity surface to the skin and the red blood cells rise up. But what was not normal was the technician's reaction during the third incision. As the patient had not reacted, he said, as if disappointed, "Well, aren't you stoic!" The patient responded that he was not stoic, but that he did not feel any pain. When the test was over, he complained to the cardiologist about the sadistic technician who loved to drill holes in people's skin.

Let's take the example of the patient who was sent to consult for abdominal pain. She had already had thirty-six operations! She was a sexy blond, very pretty, vaguely histrionic, with platinum hair, a lot of body agitation and eyes slightly spread apart.

The interview lasted four hours, after which the patient exclaimed, "I love my surgeon. I would gladly get an operation to see him!" It was clear that this behavior, which was sexual without being acknowledged as such, was pathological both in the case of the (sadistic) surgeon and in that of the (masochistic) patient, the treatment having no real use a posteriori.

Sometimes, the invasion of another's body really occurs without any act that could remind one of sexual abuse.

Lynne complained of intense anal pain. She was sent to us by her elder sister, who was twelve years older than she was and herself a psychotherapist. She had said to Lynne that even if she had not been sexually abused, she was convinced that she could be helped through the symbolic analysis of what she had experienced.

"My sister said I was sodomized by a suppository at the age of two," she explained. Upon examination, Lynne showed practically no anomalies, at least not enough to justify the intensity of her complaint. She had a few minimal, external hemorrhoids with no complications. One had burst, causing a miniscule hematoma, a blood clot under the skin, which was trivial compared to her suffering with her husband.

Yet, what an impact it had on her life! "My husband has had enough. I don't want to lose him. This pain is getting in the way of our quality of life. He has put me against the wall. Last year, we spent six months without touching each other. At our age, it is easy to cross the line. He said he did not want another "six months" this year. I have suffered several losses in my life. I don't want to lose him!"

And then an old memory came back. "I was two. My hemorrhoids had come out... My mother pushed them back in... I cried out... She forced in a suppository." And Lynne started crying like a little girl.

She had never gotten out her anger, nor resolved this poorly processed conflict with her mother, who died from a stroke at the age of fifty-three at church.

On a more archaic level, she explained, "I was the fourteenth child. She didn't want me. I was the only one she went to the hospital for. She was stuck there for three days because she had hemorrhoids. Of the fourteen, I'm the only one with hemorrhoids."

Lynne had anismus. She followed ten sessions of biofeedback that not only healed her, but also corrected her memory of the painful story when she was two. The pain disappeared. Now Lynne has to work on her relationship with her husband and with her sister.

Bodily invasion can be experienced as traumatic even if it is not sexual. One young girl still had a scar on her thigh from the surgeon who performed the Cesarean section that brought her to bring her into this world. An accident? Perhaps.

Chapter V

The Unloved

Evidently, the majority of children have good parents, or at least good enough parents. Others, known as resilient children, manage to overcome their childhood. Here, we will only discuss those who come asking for help.

Patricia, Whose Childhood Caught Up With Her

Patricia was forty-four years old. She linked digestive disorders to sexual ones, as she complained both of painful constipation and relatively deep vaginal pain when the man she loved penetrated her. She consulted a gastroenterologist. The latter sent her to us, mentioning both that she had been the victim of sexual abuse and that she was brilliant, an unusual comment for a referring physician to make.

Patricia had never been the victim of sexual abuse during her childhood. Nobody had physically or sexually violated her. Not her mother, not her father, no other man. But her father scared her. He was alcoholic and extremely violent with Patricia's mother and sister. However, Patricia had never been touched. Wide-eyed, she said, "At the age of eight, I was my parents' mother." She was a child who grew up prematurely with immature parents. She remembered that her angry father often ran after her and her mother (whom she was trying to protect) with a rifle pointed at them.

Patricia was married and happy. She said her husband was "the first man I can say I actually love. It's the first time in my life that I feel good with someone. I admire him." Then she added, "I've known him for six years and I've had intestinal problems for six years."

She began to cry about the loneliness of her childhood. Clearly, she had not finished mourning this unhappy period in her life. She cried nonstop for a long time, her tears were accompanied by the expression on her face and the tone of her voice. Her parents were still alive. Her mother was sixty-nine and her father seventy-one. He had sobered up but had never been tender. He didn't like to be touched. When she said this, she strangely used the masculine form for herself. She added, "He never held me." Then, rapidly, "I was the second daughter in our home. It's funny; my father called me "boy!"

Never, ever was she subjected to any sexual violence. Her story confirms that sexual abuse, as terrible as it is, is a horrible mask under which exists a much more archaic, profound and existential problem. In addition to the admiration and love she had for her husband and how well they got along, Patricia as an adult was experiencing a perfectly satisfying sex life. She had orgasms when her husband penetrated her. She had already cried during orgasm. She also had laughed.

From time to time, she had terrible nightmares, in which she was being chased. She couldn't describe who was chasing her. An internal censor always woke her up. In a sweat, she would wake up her husband, crawl into his arms, and was not able to go back to sleep without consolation.

At the age of seventeen, Patricia had met a young man who was nineteen. He was schizophrenic and manic-depressive. He raped her very often. This lasted for nearly seven years. One day, after having sex, he strangled her, leaving her for dead. He then ran off into the woods and shot himself in the head.

After this suicide, Patricia collected lovers. This time, she was the one who ran the show. One of them was a South American immigrant. They had a child, a son, who today was fifteen. She never talked about her son. The father had disappeared long ago. For four years, Patricia also lived a passionate relationship with a man a little older than she was. He frequently sodomized her.

"Excuse me, but that relationship was just about sex," she exclaimed, "He only thought about that. He only talked about that."

Then she fell ill. Just as she began a happy relationship, she started having trouble defecating. She suffered from what doctors call dyschezia: the anus does not open up during defecation. This symptom is probably caused by anismus.

The situation got worse after four years. Patricia developed painful Irritable Bowel Syndrome. This time, she experienced extreme pain in her belly. Only bowel movements could relieve her. Constipation always accompanied her pain. Her stools were harder than normal, difficult to expel, requiring a lot of effort. In addition, she felt bloated, and the bloating only diminished if she had a satisfactory bowel movement.

Through her quest for love, Patricia managed to grow socially and to become autonomous financially. After many years of study, she rose up the ranks and ended up running a press relations department for a large company in the suburbs of Paris.

Then she began having sexual disorders. "One evening, around eight, we were making love. I was lying on my back. He was standing. Suddenly, when he was in me, I feel a raw pain in my vagina, halfway to the uterus. It was like a wound that just came back to life." Since that day, Patricia suffered from dyspareunia, pain upon penetration, every time she had sexual intercourse. It had lasted nearly nine months. Often, even very often, as it occurs in three fourths of the cases, women who, like Patricia, suffer from Irritable Bowel Syndrome have abdominal pain during and after sexual relations (Guthrie, 1987 (page 130). But that was not her case. Her pain was strictly vaginal.

More than once during the course of the interview, Patricia frenetically cleared her throat. Yet, she did not have a cold. She said that she occasionally suffered from gastro-esophageal reflux, a dysfunction that leads to a little gastric acid rising up into the throat. But she added that this never happens during an interview and very rarely during the day. The frenetic clearing of her throat occurred particularly when she mentioned a difficult subject. Without fail, it was linked to her mother, going back to buco-pharyngeal memories, archaic memories of the time when she was breastfeeding and bottle-feeding.

Patricia ended the consultation in a strange way: "This is not the first time I have told my story. Each time, it was as if I was telling somebody else's story. Today, it is really my story. And I told it to you. But I was really frightened to go back there."

She announced where she was going, pressing forward: "I have always been a very active girl, but when I am on the ground, I don't want to do anything. I can't stop, because if I do, I'll stop everything." I visualized the image of a little girl, naked, crouched on the living room wood floor, curved over in a fetal position. Waiting…

]It seemed clear that this mature woman's childhood had just caught up with her. Finally, she was no longer obliged to spend her energy patching up the breaches of everyday life.

She only had two tests. The first measured the transit time through the large intestine. When we use objective radiological means to measure transit time, only 50% of subjects who say they are constipated are actually constipated (Wald, 1989). That means that the other half of the people who say they are constipated have perfectly normal transit times. They have many more psychological problems than the first half, whose large intestines function at a slower pace.

For Patricia, the markers transited at a perfectly normal pace. Physiologically speaking, she was not constipated. However, we did observe a small anomaly. The markers, which are small white plastic particles that can be seen on x-rays because they are radiopaque, moved right to left, towards the anus, at the level of the large intestine, and then rose towards the right on later shots. This indicated that her colon was not paralyzed, but on the contrary, the intestine was too active near the anus, and that these spasms pushed the feces towards the caecum, to the right of her intestine. So Patricia did not have colic paralysis, but a hyperactive colon, a general indicator of Irritable Bowel Syndrome.

The second test consisted of assessing the pressure in her anus and rectum. Patricia's voluntary anal contraction could be qualified as athletic. When she was asked to tighten her anus, the pressure she was able to exert was enough to move enema water up more than thirteen feet. To visualize this, she could push up a column of water higher than the ceiling of a building.

Her perineum did not lack nervous response, as is the case of older women who have spent their lives with anismus pushing against a closed anus, ending up deteriorating the muscles of the perineum by stretching the pudendal nerves.

Patricia had anismus, as was expected considering that her first lover had raped her. This anismus was particularly strong around the perineum, where she was able to exert such pressure. She strained well, but since she had closed the top of her anal sphincter, she completely contradicted the order given to defecate.

Finally, her rectum had very little sensitivity. When it was dilated with a small balloon, we observed that she had very little tolerance between feeling the sensation and feeling pain, as if she were "frozen." It reminded us of dissociation. We had already raised this possibility when Patricia said she was telling somebody else's story. A rectometrogram, which studies the pressure exerted during dilation of the rectum, confirmed that her body also dissociated in terms of sensitivity. This distancing between her body and her emotions corresponds to dissociations that Patricia experienced during the repeated rapes by her first husband.

In addition, she would also be facing the terror she must have felt as a child while her father, rifle in hand was chasing after her and her mother. All this evidence concurs to show that Patricia suffered from childhood trauma, and that this trauma was not sexually related, as with most of the cases we have described in this book.

Patricia returned three weeks later, transformed from having told her true story.

After a week, she said, the pain she had felt deep in her vagina had moved to the surface, around the vulva, like a bubble rising up to the surface. But there was something that Patricia did not understand. After our first interview, for a week, every time that she got into her car to go to work, she broke out into tears and cried for the whole trip. We could get lost guessing why. Did she consider the car to be a protective space, like a little girl who had returned to the maternal uterus? Did she consider it a place that was hers alone? And why did it only last for a week?

Patricia spent five days without a bowel movement. Then she alternated huge stools and small "balls", like those some patients call "rabbit turds." These often indicate either the presence of diverticula or of strong contractions in the colon that cut up the feces into small, smooth, round balls three to four centimeters in diameter, also characteristic of Irritable Bowel Syndrome.

Her unconscious had forewarned us that she had worked very hard to flee her existential misery. Her occupational physician prescribed sick leave for burn-out, which is another word for depression. She slept all the time.

We recommended biofeedback to treat her anismus. One session was enough to correct the dysfunction. At the same time, her vaginismus also disappeared. The abdominal pain that caused her so much suffering also diminished. Paradoxically, the biofeedback appointments, which were with a woman, were attended only erratically. Patricia cancelled several of them without any plausible excuse.

She asked for hypnosis and was refused. As Patricia was willful, her request, rightly or wrongly, had been considered as an attempt to control the therapeutic relationship. As an alternative, we suggested a session of EMDR (Eye Movement Desensitization and Reprogrammation), a technique that is often used with patients that were subjected to severe trauma. It uses visual, acoustic and kinesthetic stimulus on the right and left sides of the brain in order to try to rebalance any possible lateralization asymmetry of traumatic memories.

During this experience, Patricia predominantly experienced great anger at all she had lived through. We could deduce that this anger had been masked by her sexual and digestive disorders. On her own, Patricia realized that her poor compliance and relational difficulty with the biofeedback therapist resulted from the fact that a woman—finally— was taking care of her. Patricia as a girl had protected her mother as if she had been the mother. "I feel bad when others give of their time to me," Patricia explained, "The feeling I have is that I was born to take care of others. And I felt that my mother was really scared to take care of me."

Two months later, she called for another appointment. She

was smiling and beautiful. For the first time in her life, she had a perfectly normal, formed stool. Unusually long, it was about 20 inches long. She had just emptied the left part of her large intestine in one movement. On that day, Patricia had no traces of Irritable Bowel Syndrome. This is so sufficiently rare among normal subjects as to be noted. She said that she was so excited that she felt like a child and ran to tell her husband the good news. She no longer had abdominal pain, was hardly ever bloated, had no further sexual problems. From then on, she sometimes had a bowel movement every day for a full week, after she went to see the woman accompanying her biofeedback. She returned to work. She spent her nights dreaming of saving people. At her own initiative, she brought the meeting with the doctor to an end, thanked him, got up, kissed him on the cheek and left. She did not make another appointment.

The nature of Patricia's traumatism was clearly not of a sexual nature. As a child, on the surface, she helped her mother, but deep down, she lived like an orphan without parents. In a way, the repeated rapes she experienced between the ages of eighteen and twenty-five had served as a brutal awakening, pulling her out of a childhood devoid of all affection.

For Want Of A Mother

"I came to see you because of a dream. My dead brother took me onto his knees. He said I had intestinal problems, that I have to see three doctors and that the fight is not over." In fact, Laura was sent for a consultation because she had a bellyache and was constipated. The surgeon who sent her to us had removed a minuscule polyp from the uppermost part of her colon, near her appendix. When viewed under a microscope, the polyp's characteristics proved to be benign, but could have led to cancer.

Her brother had been dead for twenty years. When she was twelve, she broke a few ribs in a car accident. Six months later, her brother committed suicide. Since the accident, Laura has had a terrible phobia of cars. Too terrified to drive, she never got her driving license. Whenever she was in a car, she was stressed, tense, in a state of hyper-vigilance, on edge. Her right side still hurts, twenty years after the accident. She added that this side was very fragile. But she also had several other symptoms.

Her heart beat wildly. She breathed too quickly and sometimes fainted due to hyperventilation. She had pain and tightening in her chest. She had pulsating headaches on both sides when she had bowel movements. She had to urinate all the time. Penetration hurt her, and when she made love and had an orgasm, her belly was painful: "The pain is horrible after a good orgasm. It's like a deception. I feel emptied." Sometimes she cried after making love. She never laughed.

In addition to her sexual problems, she had extremely abundant periods. Her cycle was short and her period lasted ten days, with a lot of pain and clots. She had had a lot of contact with gynecologists. She had a laparoscopy at the age of fifteen, another at the age of sixteen and a third laparoscopy at the age of eighteen.

At twenty-two, she managed nevertheless to have a child. Her son, eleven at the time of her consultation, came with her to her first appointment. She had already allowed another gynecologist to convince her to have a hysterectomy. Since then, she has regretted having the operation that took away any possibility of having another child. Of course, the pathologist had found her uterus to be normal upon examination after surgery.

Her relationship to doctors was difficult and chaotic. Laura was qualified as "non-compliant." She wouldn't show up for appointments without even canceling them. For a long time, she refused any kind of test, examination or medication. Frustrated, her regular doctor sent her to see a psychiatrist he recommended. When she got to the appointment, the psychiatrist noted, "The patient does not understand the utility of consulting a psychiatrist, and neither do I. She has no demands and no suffering. A psychiatric evaluation does not appear to be necessary. You need to give more details."

Laura lived in the suburbs of a large city. Through the appointments kept, she began nevertheless to talk a little bit about her life. There was a history of sexual abuse, but she did not elaborate on the abuse, nor give any details or formulate what it was. She said she was abused at the age of three, but explained that is what she had been told. She herself had no memory of the incident. She had a history of abuse at the age of eight, when a fifteen-year-old brother fondled her. She complained to her parents and the problem stopped there, but she had never been able to settle things with her brother. It was he who had committed suicide at the age of twenty-five.

The father of her son also died at the age of twenty-five, but from a car accident. When she herself was twenty-five, she showed up at the emergency room claiming to have been raped by someone she didn't know. She had gone to a bar, and ended up alone on the bed in a hotel. She had no memory of being raped, just a feeling of deep disgust. The doctors who examined her found no trace of sperm, and no objective evidence of the alleged rape.

She said that two of her sisters had also been abused and that their stories only recently were removed from the vault of family secrets. Their telling caused their father to be hospitalized from a heart attack. And finally, she had had repetitive nightmares since she was a teenager, in which she was raped, killed and disemboweled.

The first psychiatrist had refused to see her. But because Laura was having mystical-religious dreams, we asked for a second psychiatric consultation, in order to ensure that she did not have any severe mental problems. After all, she did come from a family where a brother was schizophrenic and a sister used a lot of tranquilizers. After a much patient effort, and a threat of discontinuing treatment, Laura finally accepted the referral to a second psychiatrist. In a worrying dream, a woman told her to protect herself and close the windows.

A voice said to her, "Laura, I am Mark. Trust me. Follow me. Take your faith, cross over and join me." Mark was her dead brother. On that same day, creating more confusion, she said she thought that her father was not her father, but that her maternal grandfather had conceived with her mother. Laura also stated that her mother, who was totally absent during her childhood, had conceived 15 children Laura being the last, often said to Laura she was her little girl.

When speaking to the second psychiatrist, Laura described her father as cheerful, respectful, gentle, good, and affectionate, while describing her mother as aggressive, closed, and authoritative. Despite this association of a father full of qualities with a mother who had none, she said they got along very well.

After an in-depth evaluation of her childhood, the psychiatrist, noting the history of abuse, concluded that despite everything, the patient was not delirious, was not having hallucinations, illusions or suicidal or homicidal ideas, and despite the feelings of strangeness, he only saw a few post-traumatic signs in this woman, who had a hysterical personality structure. He said what was obvious on a medical level, "her body spoke."

He described her as very sensitive to loss and disaster, the only thing to watch for might be her tendency towards dissociation. He said that psychotropic medication would not be of any help to the patient because of her personality structure, and suggested that she continue supportive therapy.

A second medical opinion from a gastroenterologist resulted in about the same conclusions, the specialist going as far as to suggest that Laura did not need psychotherapy.

That is when she confided that she felt completely disincarnated (Barral, 1999). "I am a digestive tract with two legs. I can't seem to feel good in my body. And at night, I have nightmare upon nightmare. I have been in my body for 45 years and I'm not at all at ease there. It is too small. It has suffered too much. When I was six years old, I asked my mother about death and life. I was afraid of being poisoned." She also said she had been traumatized by numerous histories of cancer among her uncles and aunts, both on her mother's and father's side. In reaction to this heavy background, she became a vegetarian.

Laura began to improve on a symptomatic level. Her last bellyache occurred on the day her father was buried. Her belly was hard for an entire week. She had no bellyaches after his death. The difficulties with the doctor ended up being clarified once the doctor had her see a second psychiatrist. She talked about how wise she had been as a child, to have perceived the infantile nature of her mother, which was verbalized when the latter said her mother felt more like her daughter than her mother.

"My father always had to take my mother's anger. When I was very little, I knew that she was not reacting to my father, but to her own father. He was an alcoholic. When my father came back from work and had a drink when he got home, she had a fit, but I knew that in reality she was getting angry at her own father." Then she recalled her father with a lot of tenderness: "I could listen to him for hours on end…"

And she repeated what she said at the beginning: "At first, it was a dream that led me to make an appointment with you. My dead brother took me on his knees. He said that I had an intestinal problem and that I had to see three doctors. The fight is not over…"

Nobody In Front, Nobody Behind

Frances lived alone. Her mother became psychotic at her birth. She was hospitalized for the rest of her days with schizophrenia. Frances's father was alcoholic. When his wife was committed, he divorced her and put his daughter in a foster home. For a long time, she had no contact with him. When she was forty, she learned that he had committed suicide with a gun, twenty years after her birth.

Right from the start, Frances said her problem was loneliness. She had been plagued with intestinal pain since she was little, almost since birth according to the people who took care of her, and she knew the pain was linked to the abandonment.

When she was eight, her father took her from the foster home and placed her with one of his sisters, a severe woman who never showed her any tenderness. This woman's husband started "fondling" her, to use Frances's choice of words, and also "fondled" by her, without ever raping her.

Once, she read a book about the meaning of bellyaches, and it made a big impression on her. She decided to go see the author, a doctor. Very quickly, the pain disappeared.

She met a man visiting from out of town and fell madly in love with him. She left to live with him in his hometown, and then they moved back. But he was hard to export, and was very nostalgic about his hometown. One day, he decided to leave, in theory temporarily, to visit back home. Despite her desire to have children, she had not had a child with him. Very quickly after he got back "home", he fell in love with a woman born and raised there, and they had a child. Frances then began to have had suicidal ideas and dove back into her abandonment syndrome, with terrible abdominal pain.

Then Frances ran into Gerard, a former love from her youth who had adopted two Haitian children. She thought she could have a family with him. But Gerard reproached her for being emotional. She got along well with him in terms of tenderness and sexuality. Yet, she had an impressive dream in which, quite contrary to her reality, she dreamed that she could not give her companion an erection. Their relationship collapsed. Gerard left her. She fell into a deep depression, with a feeling of extreme loneliness. "There is nobody in front of me, and there is nobody behind me," she said. That is when she started having dreams of premonition. She dreamed that her brother drowned just a short time before he did. She dreamed about the death of a colleague's father shortly before he actually died. She did not seem frightened by these dreams.

She realized that the most intense part of her abdominal pain, the part that made her suffer the most, began when she met her husband. She wrote a letter that she sent to the uncle who had fondled her and released her emotions. She started therapy with a woman psychotherapist, but was uncomfortable about seeing two caregivers at the same time.

She dreamed about her personal doctor. Even though she was at home, she heard him laugh with his patients in the next room. In this dream, she also saw a redheaded guy. Then an old memory came to mind. A redhead boy, along with one of her brothers, had "played doctor" with her when she was seven. In the dream, when the doctor came near her, he was enormous and looked like Zorba the Greek.

She said she had read a tarot card that spoke about Zorba the Buddha as an ideal, joining Eastern Buddhist values with Western incarnation values. In her dream, the doctor called her "honey." He told her to stand in a doorframe with no door. He told her she was not working well with him, and he knelt before her because he was so much bigger than she was. He kissed her chest, although she didn't feel anything sexual, only affection. Water ran off the ceiling of the house, flooding the floor, and spilling out of the cellar just in front of the house. She recognized the door handle on the door to the cellar as one from her real house.

After the dream, Frances no longer had abdominal pain every day. She already considered this to be a miracle. She now had periods without pain, which lasted several days. Now that it is intermittent, her pain will serve as a guide for her.

From Illness To Identity

Violet had been going to see her doctor for fifteen years. "I'm OK; I don't have any more problems. Would you still see me again even if I don't have any physical disorder? I would like to talk to you about my difficulties being a woman."

Yet, fifteen years earlier, it was an inflammation of her rectum that led Violet to seek help. At the time, she had had Crohn's disease for six years. She asked for a second medical opinion. In fact, every year, on a repetitive anniversary date, in autumn, Violet experienced an outbreak of her illness so severe that she was hospitalized every time. Violet had two children: a little girl of five and a little boy of two. To be just like Mom, the little girl had stomachaches, but she had no proctitis linked to Crohn's. Violet's husband was very supportive. Right from the first visit, Violet made an association between her husband and her father, who she said had never accepted her.

A few days after the first visit, the same doctor performed an endoscopy of her rectum and her colon. He decided to first do a test to verify that she did in fact have proctitis, an inflammation of the rectum, due to Crohn's Disease. Sometimes this illness can resemble other types of intestinal inflammation. When he was convinced that she in fact had Crohn's Disease, he gave her two enemas and prepared to perform an endoscopy with a colonoscope, to see how high up the lesions went into the large intestine. But fifteen minutes later, she had a fit of hysterics, and told the doctor that she felt raped by the proctoscopy.

She had remembered something that she had completely blocked previously. She remembered the enemas she had been given when she was little, because she had worms. She also said later that the proctoscopy provoked her period, two weeks ahead of schedule, even though her cycle was usually perfectly regular. After saying that her parents had only been interested in her when she was sick; she then categorically refused the colonoscopy.

Violet recounted a little bit of her past. Before developing Crohn's Disease, she had been constipated for a long time. She also said she came from a family of constipated people. She only had bowel movements once a week. Occasionally, patients switch from severe and chronic constipation, lasting for decades, to severe Crohn's colitis. Any time she was constipated, it was her husband who had given her enemas. Admittedly, he would have liked to sodomize her, as he had with women before her, but she had always refused.

She had left her parents for the first time at the age of nineteen, leaving to go live with a married man. As soon as she arrived to join her lover, she started having headaches and nausea. When she developed Crohn's Disease, her mother said to her bluntly that it "served her right," implying that she had developed this disease because she had left to live with that married man.

Violet became asymptomatic after the proctoscopy provoked her period ahead of schedule. She spent most of her appointments distancing herself from her parents. She made several slips of tongue. One day, wanting to talk about her children, she said her "parents." On another day, speaking about her father, she said "I took myself into my arms" instead of "I took him into my arms." Her mother was very jealous of her studies and, most of all; jealous of the relationship she had with her father. She said that she felt unbelievable rage and hatred against her parents rising inside her. "I would have preferred not having been born into this family."

Moreover, she remembered having often asked her parents when she was little whether she had been adopted. She had little control over her emotions. During her appointments, she sometimes started screaming over the fact that she never felt loved by her parents, and that they only got close to her when she was sick. She therefore had a colossal secondary gain from remaining ill in order to keep her parents' love, which had been so lacking up until now.

Always dressed in black, she suffered more and more anxiety, but her intestine became silent. She no longer had any abdominal pain, or diarrhea, or loss of blood from the anus. However, she began to have a strange feeling of being split in two. "It's like there's another person, in the process of being born, who is in here, too." She often spoke of herself using the masculine form, without realizing there was any identity confusion.

She also added that she had had a lot of very tender, nonsexual, relationships with homosexuals. She started dreaming about her doctor. Among other things, with his help she managed to get out of a tunnel by crossing through some water. Her sexuality with her husband began to vacillate. In another dream, a stranger raped her. While he does it, she kills him with a revolver. She said she wanted to fill the emptiness as she became aware of it.

Four months after the first visit, Violet talked to her doctor, in French, using the familiar, informal form of address: "Did you notice this is the second time I came to see you without crying? I don't need to see you anymore. I have the impression that I had been in a shell since I've been sick. And the shell has opened." At this time, she had one or two solid, perfectly normal stools a day and was totally asymptomatic.

For fifteen years, she showed up for her appointments punctually, but only when she decided, and never when called by her doctor. Exactly one year after having left her doctor, during the anniversary period of her usual Crohn's Disease outburst, she showed up to tell her doctor that she had gone through her first winter without an episode. She was thrilled. And she told him, "It makes me feel good to be in charge of my own life." She added that she had gone to see her parents for a week and that during this week she had had colic, like a baby.

Five years later Violet came back for a few appointments. There was a lot of tension in her relationship. Both of them were unemployed. She realized that every time she bled from the rectum, she experienced a great feeling of love lost, and this time she associated her parents with her husband. She refused all tests and prescriptions, as she would for a long time.

Another three years later she came back. This time, she was bleeding abundantly from the rectum. She was waiting to have a hysterectomy because she also had painful, abundant, difficult periods. A gynecologist who was rather liberal in prescribing hysterectomies had recommended one.

Violet's mother, sister and mother-in-law, all three of whom had had hysterectomies, were placing a lot of pressure on her to give up her uterus. The three women proclaimed: "You'll see how good you feel when you don't have a uterus anymore!" This time, in a crisis, she agreed to have intensive medical treatment.

After some thought, she decided to refuse the hysterectomy. She asked for a second opinion from another gynecologist, who said he did not agree with the need for an operation, reassuring her in her decision to refuse surgery. She stopped taking her medication, without asking anyone's opinion. Her symptoms did not return.

Once again, she stopped her appointments for three years. However, this time Violet did not come to ask for advice and had the hysterectomy after all. It was performed by a female gynecologist, who looked very much like a man. The decision to operate had in fact been very reasonable, as Violet had a small, benign tumor of the uterus that had doubled in size in one year. She had no regrets. Months later, her abdominal pain began again, worse this time, and she started to excrete bloody mucus, glair, with pus, in her stools.

She talked for a long time about her relationships with her father, her mother and her husband. When she was little, her father was often absent because of his work. It was her mother who was in charge in the family.

Violet herself said that she mothered her spouse, except when she was sick. At these times, the roles were inversed, and he "mothered" her. Through the years, she had advanced a lot socially. She had studied to be a psychologist. She had even received an award of excellence from her university. Yet she had remained very unsure of herself. She said she always had to perform to please her parents.

Her own seventeen-year-old daughter deeply moved her when she told Violet she found her "inaccessible." In fact, Violet had a lot of trouble letting go of her emotions, and yet she nevertheless had orgasms when she and her husband made love, both with penetration and caresses. Once again, she refused all tests and examinations. And her doctor noted in her file, "She most certainly has deep identity problems and no interiorized masculine image."

Again she took another three-year break.

When she came back on the day of her birthday, she was again losing blood through her digestive tract. She had treated herself with cortisone enemas and had not asked for any professional advice. With those treatments, she had managed to control the pain. She had formed stools one to three times a day. She was put on sick leave, which began on the same date she began to work as a psychologist in a company, exactly three years earlier. She had no long-term regrets about having lost her uterus, because the quality of her life had improved greatly since then. But she had stopped mothering her spouse.

Violet was experiencing a lot of emotion. Sadness led her to anger and to rivers of tears. "It goes back and forth between the head and the belly." She had moments of emptiness and despair. Her daughter, who had left, returned home. She took up a lot of space. This reminded Violet of her own family where she hadn't had a place. She had been her family's fifth child. She found that her husband was soft, and that she herself couldn't manage to say no. She observed that she was eating and drinking a lot. "I'm filling up a vacuum." She decided to go see a psychotherapist.

As her symptoms were severe, it was necessary to perform an endoscopy. At the first appointment, she was extremely reticent about undergoing the rectal examination. The doctor took a paradoxical approach, a kind of "proctodrama." He suggested that she draw a picture of herself with and without the illness, and after this, the test was postponed.

Two weeks later, since the symptoms had not disappeared, she agreed to have a colonoscopy—for the first time in fifteen years! There was no blood in the bowel. There were normally colored, formed stools in the colon. Her illness was active on about ten centimeters of the intestine. She had numerous scars indicating that she had already had very active colitis. The central and right parts of the colon were perfectly normal. After the colonoscopy, she cried for a long time. Her sobbing sounded like that of a very little girl. The crying had started before the endoscopy, increased during it, and multiplied even more afterwards. She expressed her deception at not having managed to control her illness alone. On this day, she accepted adequate medical treatment. She was also sent to see a therapist known to be able to help people express their anger.

One week later, she returned, transformed, saying that she had never realized to what extent it was difficult to let go, and how she had for fifteen years maintained absolute control over the management of her illness and of the doctor-patient relationship. For the first time, she also said that she did not know how to feel joy, and that she had never been taught to allow herself to feel pleasure. She had experienced the prescription of medication literally as punishment.

"The next day, I felt this taste of death, not a desire to commit suicide, but to die." On this day, we learned that she not only had a twenty-year-old daughter, but that she also had an eighteen-year-old son, whom she had never mentioned in fifteen years.

Through a crisis with her spouse, Violet learned to appreciate him: "I chose my spouse well. He listens to me a lot. He puts no pressure. He does not send me back to my father. He is good." And this time, she acknowledged a difference between him and his parents, adding that he had a child inside him who had no trouble at all feeling joy. All her biochemical tests were normal.

She accepted a colonoscopy for verification and at the same time she stopped her medication. This test occurred without any complications or pain. Her endoscopy showed that she was in complete remission. She herself called this period an "existential crisis" and said that she had touched a much deeper layer of herself. Violet added that she thought she had really made peace with her parents.

She realized that her daughter was now the age she had been when she left her parents to go live with the married man. "I resolved this issue. I had a miserable time finding my place. The last years, I felt completely lost," she said, in a very clear reference to an anniversary syndrome.

Violet also started having dreams of premonition. She was not particularly surprised, just happy to note that this was happening. At this time she asked if she could still see the doctor to talk about her female identity problems even if she was no longer sick.

This raises the question of how the body speaks its ills to a physician taking care of the body, and how people hesitate starting psychotherapy. The Freudian heritage has left a great number of "orthodox" psychoanalysts, who are ill informed about current research and still deny family incest in order to blame everything on the Oedipus Complex, remaining believers in the fantasy theory, as if in total transference on Sigmund Freud, a dead psychoanalyst.

According to Joyce McDougall, all human beings need to mourn the difference between psychic bisexuality and bodily mono-sexuality (McDougall, 1995). From this arises the issue of the difference, which occurs on a cerebral level, between the corporal (anatomical, surgical) body image, the imaginary body full of fantasies and bodily deformations, and the unconscious body image, which is much more relational.

The Unloved

All the stories recounted in this chapter have something in common that goes beyond the issue of sexual abuse, which for us was just an entry point to explore the traumatisms inflicted upon the children. They also have in common the fact that, from the beginning of their lives, the subjects did not feel recognized or loved. If there is one word that had become trite in everyday language, it is "love." We can be loved by ourselves, for ourselves or loved as a thing like a cake that you love to eat. Parents who are "parentified" and who use their children like parents, therapists or canes for their old age, say that they "love" them.

All human beings, in all countries, cultures and religions, seek to be loved. Men as much as women. Unfortunately, very often, "to love" means "to love oneself" through another, which is a very "selfish" expression of a "narcissistic" subject, stemming from a wound rooted in a very huge lack of love and leading the person to project his or her own emotional deficiencies on others, the first targets being his or her children.

There is no love without respecting the difference, the absolute otherness of the other.

Today we know that a newborn child remembers the sound of his or her mother's voice. It is she who sings lullabies while the child is still in her womb, and when the child is just barely born, he or she prefers to suckle to this sound before all others, thus using his digestive tract for emotional ends rather than digestive ends. Psychoanalyst Didier Dumas, in looking back at the story of Cain and Abel, the executioner and his brother the victim, postulated that in the beginning of their relationship, Adam and Eve made love without speaking about love (Dumas, 2001). But that is another story…

Could it be that the greatest trauma of all for a child is to have been conceived without love?

Chapter VI

Anniversary Syndromes,
Unspeakable Traumas
and Unfinished Bereavement

What cannot be expressed in words remains in the body and expresses itself through pain and illness. When wounds are insurmountable, unspeakable, they leave traces. What cannot be expressed persists and is transmitted. What is somatized persists in the body of the child and the grandchild or the great-grandchild can become the wounded ancestor's means of expression, the spokesperson of that ancestor's traumatisms.

Bleeding From The Truck

Paul's children (Dominique and Tom) remembered that sometimes he spoke to them about the war in Algeria and told them the shock he experienced one summer day when, after a violent skirmish, he saw a truck full of dead and wounded drive by. Blood was dripping out the back. It was the blood of one of his buddies, who was bleeding to death. It reminded him of his grandfather in Verdun, during the First World War. He too had lost numerous cousins and friends under horrible conditions, unforgettable and unforgotten.

Trucks and roads were Paul's father's life. His grandfather, and before him his great grandfather, even tended sheep along the roads in the high mountain pastures. Paul himself founded his own transport company, but his two children wanted to go into different professions, in other places, to *renounce their heritage.*

One summer, Paul died. Ten years later, his son Tom began "to bleed from the behind". It was summer again. He was immediately hospitalized. He was discovered to have a serious case of Crohn's disease. Some doctors think this disease may be linked to a hereditary element, although there is only weak scientific evidence of the connection. Nevertheless, Tom decided to leave the hospital and began to inquire about the possible family-related causes of his illness. He was tired, discouraged about being on sick leave and had to completely stop all his sports and professional activities.

Tom talked about his past for a long time. He immediately remembered the "truck that bled from behind". He worked intensely on this image, and then on his family history, the roads, the blood and the "bleeding to death." He proceeded to metabolize and digest all of this horror, expressing his emotion, taking up his life again and finding the strength to go on.

One week later, his sister, Dominique, had what seemed to be an attack herself. For a few hours, she was mute. She couldn't get a word out. Then she remembered what her brother had been working on, and the death of their father. The next day, she felt better. It seemed that this malaise was a way to remember the ten-year anniversary on the exact day as the stroke that cut down her father Paul a few weeks before he died of cancer. Dominique unconsciously reproduced all the symptoms. Clearly, she experienced what we call Anniversary Syndrome. She felt reassured and she reassured her doctor.

The next day, traumatized, she spoke about it again. She felt as if a story not her own was crossing through her. The story belonged not to her, but to those close to her, to her family.

We proposed that she continue to love her father, that she continue to be loyal to him, but that she return to him his physical symptoms, because where he was now, he could no longer suffer from them.

But such a proposition, putting words to it, was not enough to change things. As a precautionary measure, she had a brain scan. They found a brain tumor that proved to be cancerous. The operation went well, even surprisingly well. She recovered all of her faculties very quickly. We spoke about this together. An Anniversary Syndrome was obvious to her.

The two children had renounced their professional heritage and the family business, but nobody had thought of any other heritage they might have received. Indeed, each had inherited, or taken as their heritage, different manifestations of their father's mortal illness. That message got across and they each worked things through. As the body healed so did the soul, returning the father's illness to the past, and ending the bereavement with renewal. [Note: See Chapter 7 for more clinical observations of Dominique].

The Knocked-Over Child

Maria was an old-timer, who came back to see us about family problems. Her mother had fallen ill from cancer and died. Maria had remained in the group to get help. She was typically Mediterranean: a tall, beautiful brunette skilled in the arts, gardening, and cooking. She had a heart of gold, was well behaved, kind and discreet. She worked in the service of others and earned her own living.

Of Italian origin, she had a terrible family history with several generations of abandoned, illegitimate children, who were often abused, beaten, and wounded.

On his good days, her father showed off his back, scarred from the wounds received as a child in various foster homes. On his bad days, he became his foster parents. He cried out, screamed, raged, beating his children and abusing them. Maria had spent her life falling asleep terrorized, watching the door, and dreading seeing her father. Maria had a son, who was also born out of wedlock. At school, the big kids abused him and beat him up. Through psychotherapy and psychodrama she made peace with her parents, who had grown gentler with age.

A new drama broke out. Her aged mother died of cancer at the hospital. The family forgot to tell Maria where she was. Maria spent a long time looking for the hospital, but arrived too late. She did not get to see her mother alive again.

The following morning, Maria got a call from her aunt who was frightened. She had been standing in front of Maria's father's door, which was locked. She asked Maria to open it with her key because her father would not respond to her knocking. To her horror, she discovered her father had hung himself. She cut him down gently, then buried him but never got over it.

This man had said that he would not live longer than his wife and promised to kill himself after her death. But the fact that his daughter had to take the dead body in her arms to lay him out on his bed was also a violation of her personal body space and indirectly another abuse of his power. So her father made her suffer even after his death. This latest violence kept her from grieving her mother. Her father had revived all of her earlier traumatisms.

In psychodrama reenactment, Maria worked for a long time through the different phases, using surplus reality to say goodbye to her mother by arriving minutes before her death at the hospital. That way she could say goodbye to her mother. She said a final goodbye to her father next and placed her parents' ashes together in a pretty urn and planted a rose bush in their garden above their urn… symbolically, psycho-dramatically, in a therapeutic act of release.

But none of this was enough. She continued to have nightmares. She felt the weight of the dead body and the odor in her nostrils.

She continued with group psychodrama.

Nearly two years later, she participated in a three-day residential Psychodrama Workshop and spoke about her respiratory difficulties. She was specific. It was like she had a stone on her chest.
    "What type of stone?"
    "Sandstone."

"What kind of sandstone? What shape?"
"Rectangular."
"What is it?"
"A tombstone."
"Whose tombstone?"
"My little brother's."
We backed up.

When she was twelve or thirteen, from a distance, Maria saw her little brother down the road on his bike hit full on by a truck, thrown across the road, then moved and dragged into the neighboring field by the trucker, whom she then saw flee the scene.

She had remained paralyzed, voiceless, petrified, and unable to move, scream, or cry. When she was able to go down, call for help and have her dying brother hospitalized, it was too late. He died at the hospital.

During her therapy we had already worked on this at length, but the dramatic death of her father had been such a great shock that it took her breath away for months, and caused nightmares. She had regressed back to the death of her brother.

Not only was Maria anxiety-ridden and "out of sorts," but she no longer felt her "ego boundary" or "self-ego", to use Didier Anzieu's expression. That is, she no longer felt the limits of her body. The limits of her body space had been violated by the shock of this violent death. The essential traumatism of her life, the death of her little brother many years ago, had telescoped with her father's death.

We thus did some surplus reality work to psycho-dramatically remove this tombstone, to reenact her grief and bury her brother respectfully, as we observed a minute of silence; Maria placed the tombstone on the grave psycho-dramatically, and planted a rosebush on his grave psycho-dramatically. She shed very welcome and calming tears, and was finally able to open her lungs and her solar plexus and breathe.

Despite long years of professional psychodrama practice, we had decided a year prior to this, to bring this case to colleagues and ask for help under supervision. We had already played a role-playing game to remove the hung father, with an "auxiliary ego" group member playing the role of Maria.

This auxiliary ego, Nina, an experienced psychodramatist of Mediterranean background who did not know Maria or her history, role-played the experience of a repressed memory that likened the weight of the body of the dead father to the weight of a man on her when she had been sexually abused as a little girl.

Naturally, the story of this experience by the auxiliary ego person was told to the group to which Maria belonged. Maria had a black veil over her childhood.

Over the next several months, things moved forward.

The day following this episode, we worked on Maria's dreams and her improved bodily experience. Finally, to visually explain to her what "personal body space" meant, we showed Maria the famous classic drawing by Leonardo da Vinci of a man moving his arms and legs in a circle and a square. Maria then saw and understood.

Lawrence LeShan (1980) explained that after surmounting

a first serious childhood trauma, a second trauma often revives and increases the first to the point of having serious psychosomatic consequences (LeShan, 1980).

Freud also wrote, in his footnotes, that one needs to treat trauma like a symphony whose themes are used again and again and worked on various levels until you reach a final expression, a resolve, whose official end is often far from full recovery (Leader, 2000; cf. Freud, 1913, 1919, 1923). Each better needs to be treated as a stage: "You must a hundred changes try."

I follow a patient's growth, listen to him or her, allow him or her to come back to talk even when, in theory, the work is "finished"—and I listen to or see the patient without an appointment, in an emergency if necessary, or do a little extra short "slice" of therapy. I continue until everything has been worked over, worked through, or, as psychodramatists say, until one has finally had a "catharsis of integration" of the entire person, not just partial catharses.

What is hurried, done without taking the time, is not respected by time.

The Lady With The Choker

Amanda came to do a genosociogram. This technique aims not only to work on the family tree, but also, as we say in clinical psychogeneology, to do transgenerational psychological work that takes into consideration genetics, heredity, psychological history, and all the family's relational bonds over several generations.

She was an elegant woman, recognized professionally, who had an original streak and came from a very good family. What was striking upon her arrival, to an informed observer, was that she was wearing a long, beautiful scarf and a superb pearl choker, a necklace that said something.

"Your necklace is beautiful. Do you wear it often?"
"Always."
"Always? Everyday?"
"Always."
"Always?"
"I always have."
"Has someone in your family had neck problems or pain?"
"Yes, my son."
"What did he have?"
"Throat cancer."
"How old is he?"
"Thirty-four."
"How old was he when he found out he had cancer?"
"Thirty-three."
"And are there any other neck-related problems?"
"Yes, he has always had sore throats."
"Was anybody in your lineage been guillotined, decapitated or hung?"
"Decapitated."
"Who?"
"My husband's grandfather's father, my son's great grandfather."

And then we spoke about this.

Emotion, tears, recalled memories…

"He was decapitated on the town square in a provincial city

and was never buried. Just lay there like a dog, " Amanda told me.

"It is important to honor this death and to bury him with dignity. Even if we do it retroactively and symbolically nearly two centuries later."

Amanda thought about having mass said for the peace of his soul, and of placing a spray of flowers on this historical town square.

She wanted to undertake this burial ceremony with the entire family of the decapitated great-grandfather and also in the presence of her son who had the throat cancer.

A little bit later, it was as if some waves had reached the outside world: the details of the public decapitation of this man years ago reappeared in the media.

It was as if her remembering this event privately had touched the outside world. But that is another story, close to the "morphogenetic waves" of Ruppert Sheldrake, whose work on the co-unconscious, the specificity of cells and their contents, and of the propagation of ideas in the world is most important.

The Day When Ralph Rediscovered Life's Colors

Ralph was a psychologist and a psychotherapist. He worked in an institution with criminals and treated serious pathologies in his private practice. Although he seemed to have a successful career, he nevertheless carried with him a kind of recurring depression. He wasn't comfortable with himself. He was devoured by his work, and couldn't manage to have a personal, emotional life of his own for any length of time.

After several years of psychodrama, he managed to find a girlfriend and a new, easier job in another town. Nevertheless, every summer he returned to participate in psychogeneology and psychodrama workshops.

One day, on a large piece of paper taped to the wall, we drew up his family tree, including in it the events that marked the family's history over five or six generations. And when discussing the difficulties his mother experienced when she was a child, Ralph said, "Mom never got over the death of the neighbor's little boy. She used to baby sit him when she was fifteen or sixteen. She blamed herself, even though it was not her fault."

It was not her fault.

Ralph's hand trembles a little when writing this on the large piece of paper.

I grabbed onto the subject and we talked about it more. Gradually, Ralph figured out that he had been a replacement child in his mother's eyes. He replaced the dead neighbor boy for her.

We used psychodrama to play out the child's burial. We also did "surplus reality" work. Ralph played his mother. She (Ralph) asked forgiveness from the dead child for her negligence. Then, in a role reversal, Ralph played the child and responded, "I understand, but dry your tears, I am in peace now. I am not angry with you."

Ralph then returned to his own role and we finished the work. He left the room for a few minutes, and then came running back in. He opened the door, astonished, relaxed, smiling, as if lit up from inside, and asked, "Those drapes there have red tassels, right?"

"Yes."

"And over there, there's a blue line?"

"Yes."

"And they were like that before?"

"Yes."

"I never noticed."

When the salt has lost its savor, and the world its colors...

Ralph discovered a world in color! Very moved, he told us about it. Until then, for him everything was gray and dark, the color of the mourning he was living in, his mother's unfinished bereavement.

In the days and months that followed, the world of colors continued for him.

Ralph had been raised by a "dead mother," to use the expression from psychoanalyst André Green—a mother who was absent for her child, totally preoccupied by the trauma of mourning another child. Ralph paid the price for it. He had been a sad child, closed up, well behaved and nice, but everything was dark for him.

Ralph had to experience more than darkness, so he needed reds and blues in order to move on.

By doing his mother's mourning *for her*, he saved his own life. By leaving his position of replacement child, he was able to blossom into his own life, leaving the colors of death far behind him.

Here we touch on the question of invisible family loyalties that create transgenerational bonds that move across generations without any words, language, or expression of feelings: no sadness, guilt, death anxiety or shared tears having been released. The trauma, the open wound, remained unresolved in the mother, leaving her in a gray world—a world which crossed through her and touched her son. After his emotional catharsis and awareness, the son rediscovered the world of colors.

Poetic Discoveries

All traditions, all religions as well as numerous myths and tales teach us about the discoveries of popular wisdom. It is interesting to see that poets have described therapeutic clinical observations and the results of medical research long before they occurred.

Homer already had the beautiful Helen say that she saw life in full color, but that she did not see certain events. In *Tiger at the Gates*, Jean Giraudoux has Helen say, while Hector is pushing her to leave Troy in order to avoid the war that she accepted the principle, but she didn't believe it, because she could not see it in color (Giraudoux, 1955). She had followed Paris because he stood out on the sky, while her husband Martin was transparent and she couldn't see him.

Frequently, we have observed that after an important therapy session the client has a more relaxed body and face, breathes more deeply, carries himself straighter and finds the world to be brighter.

Baby Listens

We were in the Indies, and a beautiful but sad Mary, an abandoned girl-mother came to see us more to complain than to consult. Oscar, her newborn who was with her was crying day and night, and she could no longer sleep.

She complained about her husband. When he found out that I was pregnant, that bastard disappeared." (*Silence.*)

"Hmm?"

"And he's hiding, faraway, in Paris." (The baby cried and the mother sniffed).

"Your baby is beautiful." (Oscar, who was two months old, turned and "looked" at me. I smiled at him.) "And he is so well dressed. Pretty baby."

"Yes, his uncle brought him that to wear."
"His uncle?"

"His father's brother."

"He comes to see him sometimes?"

"Yes…"

"And does he help out a little?"

"He brings a little money."

"Often?"

"Actually, yes."

"You see, baby," (*I said, turning towards Oscar*), your father loves you, and he sends money so that you can be alright, and that beautiful vest so that you are handsome." *(The baby stopped crying as I spoke directly to him.)* "And what is happening between your father and your mother, that's not your problem. What is important for you is that your father loves you, sends you gifts and asks his brother to come pay attention to you."

The baby looked at his mother, looked at me and seemed to start to smile.

During the rest of the appointment, Oscar remained calm and fell asleep peacefully. A few days later the mother came back, the baby was sleeping through the night.

This is one example from many clinical cases I have seen in my practice that illustrate well the work of Françoise Dolto who says, Children know everything that is going on and hear it, …. right from birth, …. If you speak the truth to a child, he or she will calm down and sleep (Paraphrased) (Dolto, 1993).

In another case where a newborn could no longer sleep, was crying day and night, we brought to light, in the presence of his parents, the fact that he had stopped sleeping after the surgery he had had at the age of five weeks. We pointed out that the mother had nearly died at the age of five weeks as well, and that the maternal grandmother had lost a five-week-old little brother when she was four, that the great-grandfather had been abandoned and found at the age of five or six weeks, and that the father's father had been a bastard, abandoned by his parents.

Indeed, the father and mother were experiencing strong emotions while discovering this repetitive history. They were busy writing it down on their genosociogram and the baby, whose name was Nicholas, followed everything attentively, going back and forth between his mother and father's arms, stopping his crying and snuggling into his mother or father's neck.

Finally, Nicholas fell asleep, and was able to sleep peacefully during the following weeks, having integrated the message that he would not be abandoned after the terrible near death experience that he had had in the operating room.

There exists a mutual investment in the total mother-infant communication and in the exchanges of words, murmurs, looks with a child who is snuggled in his or her mother's arms while feeding. It is the co-construction of a "co-ego" (as Ada Abraham calls it), of a family co-conscious. Co-unconscious (a term Anne Ancelin Schutzenberger began using with J. L. Moreno).

The experience of the body and the intersubjective experience create an anchoring in the body that is interactive. It provides roots as it includes the family history and the parental family tree. Bion already said that thoughts were rooted in the emotional experiences of the past and that this latter is transmitted, "digested" or "raw," by the parents.

The experience is internalized, either by what Nicolas Abraham and Maria Török call "introjection" (with full representations), or by a psychic inclusion with the experience's information being enclosed in a sort of vacuole, put into a psychic closet, buried in a crypt, cut off from the rest of the personality, left in the margins of the person's psychic life (Abraham & Torok, 1978).

In these cases, a split can occur: one part of the person knows, while the other does not know, does not perceive, does not want to know.

We have spoken earlier about dissociation in cases of terror, violent trauma, rape and torture. Secrets and unspoken information create troubles of this kind.

Of Chance and Narrative Medicine

From a scientific medical approach, all the stories we have just told are nothing more than anecdotes that stem from an ancient medical practice that was made up from personal observations. As vast as they are, they were never evaluated on the basis of statistics in order to verify if a hypothesis put forth based on an experiment was exact or not. Nevertheless, as Freud thought, it is necessary to report clinical cases in order to set down milestones and to pave the way for fundamental medical research.

On the other hand, in the area of mental health, a relationship can never be founded on statistical data applied to a specific case. The limits of statistics, founded on the Gauss curve and the calculation of probabilities, never allow one to know ahead of time who will live and who will die. Each story is individual and its unfolding depends on multiple factors that are personal and linked to one's surroundings.

This is precisely the difficulty of practicing humane medicine, one that is not disincarnated. The meeting between a caregiver and someone who comes seeking help must, without exception, be a relationship between two equal subjects, and not that of a shrink (or a big boss) who knows, just like a parent who tells one how to feel better. Rather, it should be more like the opposite. The person who does not feel good about himself must take things in hand and be satisfied with being assisted. There are no pills for happiness or love.

So how can one integrate the two approaches? One must respect the other's differences and believe that growth is always possible.

Clearly, if the memory of a little brother who was killed by a truck arises much later in life and is followed by a flood of emotion, it is not because the incident had been consciously memorized, but repressed into the unconscious, as if placed alive in a dark closet. Now we can still know why a modern and elegant woman always wears a choker, or dog's collar, because centuries ago one of her ancestors was decapitated and abandoned in the streets, like a dog, still bleeding at the neck.

It would be very pretentious for a scientist to dare to affirm that this is all the fruit of chance and quite foolhardy for a psychologist to follow suit and pretend that the two are not related.

All that we can do is live with the baggage of established

scientific knowledge and follow working hypotheses with the relationship. Joséphine Hilgard has proven, at least at a psychiatric level, that the anniversary syndrome is statistically significant in certain cases of adult psychosis (Hilgard, 1989, 1963, 1953).

This should lead us to remain open-minded, and admit that although this is a "soft" science, we still inherit our family history.
Holistic medicine has always viewed illness as a part of the whole person, which includes their life experiences. The traditional scientific medical approach continues to view "illness" apart from the wholeness of an individual's life experiences.

One should always add the person's life history to the clinical case and to the classical anamnesis. Because it is this history that contains the not yet worked through traumas of our ancestors, these traumas can turn us into living mummies waiting for the day when our ancestors emotional spirits will be released.

As Willy Barral (2003) reminds us, along with Françoise Dolto (1993), it is necessary to "decode the scars inscribed in our *curriculum historique*" as far back as great grandparents because "The child's body is the language of the parents' history" (Barral, 2003; Dolto, 1993). A medicine that takes into consideration the whole person can shed light on and decode the family psycho-history (LeShan, 1989).

Chapter VII

From Generation to Generation

It is not the unthinkable traumas that we suffer from or the shocking sexual abuses, which happened to us which make us sick. It is the emotional reactions to the abuses that we, or our ancestors, endured in silence throughout lifetimes; it is the emotions and words that remained repressed over several generations that cause Post Traumatic Stress Disorder, PTSD. It is these unexpressed feelings that are often unconsciously and unwittingly transmitted from one generation to another.

Everyone experiences grieving and traumatic events in his or her own, personal, singular way. The process of grieving, as in a loss, is different for everyone. Whether a terrible event is experienced personally or publicly, in the present or several generations ago, each family has transmitted their own style of dealing with trauma, loss or abuse.

Some families have continually avoided dealing with negative feelings altogether and never have, or never will, make the opportunity to talk about the trauma to the person or to each other. Sometimes family members never talk about the trauma to anyone at all outside the family and keep the experience totally secret.

As clinicians who have been practicing transgenerational therapy for many years, what has become apparent to us is that our patients suffer most from the unfinished grieving in their families, the emotions that were kept "in denial," and the comfort that was not given. Often, people are blamed or shamed, and the necessary emotional support is withheld. Victims or survivors are often encouraged to be "strong and deal with it" in an effort to "get on with life," and "recover" much too soon, we might add.

Often the event is not talked about in an effort to "hush it up," and it is kept secret to avoid public shame or even pity or ridicule. Often this avoidance lasts several generations and it is not surprising that even two generations later, younger family members know that something happened to "Auntie so and so," but they were never told exactly what happened, how, when or to whom, specifically.

But whether it happened then or now, a family that hides the facts and do not air them by speaking or crying about them - also hides the grieving and prevents the traumatized person's recovery. The emotional reactions to shocking events, abuses or traumas need to be released for the emotional health of the person who originally experienced it - no matter when it happened, whether it is now or in the past to parents, grandparents or great-grandparents.

PSTD [PTSD] is the psychological name given to the repressed emotional shock and the terrifying flashbacks experienced by people who have repressed their normal emotional response to a trauma.

To be human is above all to know how to cry for losses and to bury the dead whether it is those who die now or those who died long ago. Current family members need to express the grief for past family members especially if those family members never felt the grieving themselves. Psychodrama techniques offer an alternate way to do this.

The case studies mentioned in this book are true stories taken from our practices. We have changed all the first names and some details to protect the anonymity of the individuals. We have given you detailed case studies of people whose bodies were somatizing the unexpressed grief and shock of a former trauma, even if it did not happen to them, but to their parent or ancestor.

Four Case Studies

Uno

Uno has just arrived in quite an emotional state from Sri Lanka where the Tsunami disaster recently occurred. Uno was born there was there on vacation visiting his family and is now experiencing the shock of having seen his childhood home with his parents in it swept away into the Indian Ocean. He is, as yet, unable to cope with his living nightmare. Indeed, it is much too early to expect him to recover from it. Uno needs to grieve and get permission to cry and wail. He will have our support and that of friends as he talks about his tragedy.

Through this normal healthy process of grieving, in time, Uno will recover from his loss if he trembles away the shock of the tragedy, screams out his fury, and cries out the sadness. As a result, Uno will always have the sad memory but not the pain. And by feeling the emotional pain, he will not have the PTSD, which would be the result if his unexpressed pain remained locked inside of him.

Ana

Let's move on to the story of Ana, a small elderly woman who was all bent over. Ana would have looked quite ordinary except that people always commented on her beautiful blue eyes which were so bright they were often compared to those of Agatha Christie's Little Miss Marple, who saw and knew "everything."

Our Ana drank her tea "A la Russe," so close to boiling, we could often see the bubbles popping up in her teacup. Yet, no matter how hot she could drink her tea, she could not tolerate hot water touching her body. The nurse, who had to bathe the old woman because Ana could no longer do so alone, was surprised at her phobia of hot water.

When we asked Ana why she was so fearful of hot water touching her, she thought about it, and suddenly remembered that her father, who was born in 1880, had lost his three-year-old little sister when he was eighteen years old. The child had been burned to death by boiling hot water when she opened a tap on a 19th Century wood burning stove in their old country house. The phobia handed down to Ana as an unconscious "invisible family loyalty," was a survival mechanism from her paternal side of the family.

Therefore, heat on the skin was perceived as deadly for any female in Ana's family because her grandmother, who had been so traumatized by this horrible accident, had never fully worked through her own grief. It did not matter whether Ana's father had witnessed the scalding or not because his emotional suffering was connected to the deep sorrow repressed by his mother.

You see, Ana 's paternal grandmother was not present when her child died and as a result, her sense of guilt for not being present still haunted her. If only she was present, perhaps her daughter would have lived, perhaps she could have saved her; instead, she had often incriminated herself.

On the maternal side of Ana 's family, drinking very hot tea had always been a traditional pleasure so she was able to do that, while bathing in hot water was taboo because of her father's mother's transgenerational trauma.

Dominique

A brain tumor had developed in Dominique ten years after her father died of cancer. The night her father passed away, Dominique was sound asleep. Although Dominique would have benefited from being able to say her last good-bye to her father, "for her own good," her mother had decided not to awaken her. Dominique's mother did not want to leave her husband's side for the amount of time it would have taken her to get her daughter up. However, as much as Dominique's mother wanted to be with her husband, she was at the brink of exhaustion and had finally succumbed to her need for sleep. Sadly, Dominique's father died alone.

Dominique, now an adult and herself a physician, was hospitalized as a result of her brain tumor (of the glioma type), and once again, had found herself agonizing over her father's death. Her brother, Tom, was also in the hospital suffering with Crohn's disease, a somatization he "coincidentally" developed on his father's birthday. Both Dominique and her brother were working with us on transgenerational issues. We had genosociogram assessments that covered over six generations of their family. We thought Dominique's tumor was somatized from her unfinished grief as a result of her not being able to say good-bye to her father.

To further support this perspective, it is worthy to note that her mother had always been jealous of the devoted love her husband had had towards his children, in particular, towards Dominique. In therapy, Dominique addressed her fear that the brain tumor would kill her sooner rather than later. Since life expectancy for those with glioma is extremely short, this was a very reasonable fear for Dominique to express.

In addition to being a physician, Dominique had always been a very active individual. She loved to ski, dance, draw, and listen to music with her friends, and she especially loved to sculpt. It was her talent for both drawing and sculpting that prompted us to suggest that she create a piece of art that represented her surviving this illness and living a long productive life. We hoped this drawing would counter her fear of death.

She interpreted our therapeutic instructions by sketching a beautiful snail that moved ever so slowly, carrying his house on his back. She also sculpted a woman wearing her oval head in her arms, a hallucinating exact representation of the medical image of the glioma, and she did it just before having surgery at Christmas.

After her open skull surgery, Dominique chose to spend Christmas in the Intensive Care Unit even though it was not absolutely indicated at that time. However, Dominique preferred not to face her mother and chose to say she had to stay in the hospital rather than have to join the family for Christmas dinner, even though her mother was adamant about Dominique's attendance there.

A drastic, socially acceptable method of distancing...

Facing those extremely rare occurrences of survival against all odds, very often, the family and people close by give up, and, unconsciously, provoke what they feared. Until the tensions between Dominique and her family flared up again, Dominique was enjoying her life away from them. However, one week later, she was buried.

Twin Studies

Let us not forget that stress is lived differently depending on whether it is a personal real life experience or felt in sympathy for a loved one. Some people suffer more when pain is experienced by someone they love than when it is their own real pain. American twin studies by Rachel Yehuda (1995) showed that when one twin stayed in the United States while the other went to war, the stress, measured by their amount of cortisol, was greater in the twin left at home (Yehuda, 1995).

The twin who was not at war experienced more emotional stress in his body than did the twin actually in the real war. The amount of cortisol is much higher during emotional stress than during actual stress. As terrible as the stress was for the twin who was soldiering, the emotional stress was far worse for his brother that had stayed at home and worried constantly.

The famous classical French writer, Madame de Sevigne (1626-1696) wrote to her daughter, Madame de Grignan, who had bronchitis: "I suffer from your chest." She was imagining and suffering more than her sick daughter.

Jane - Psychodramatic Surplus Reality

Jane was an illegitimate child given up by her mother at birth and placed for adoption. The identity of her birth mother was withheld from Jane as a result of adoption laws imposed at that time. Jane grew to adulthood still holding onto a compelling desire to locate her birth mother. We suggested that Jane attend the psychodrama workshop we were presenting in order to grieve her birth mother.

The process that occurs during psychodrama work involves creating a "surplus reality," that is, an alternate reality that imagines and reconstructs a past memory. This work is especially effective when an individual carries within them unmet needs emanating from unresolved situations.

Psychodrama as a therapeutic technique can be very helpful in uncovering repressed secrets and releasing repressed needs. This is accomplished by using current emotions to locate unmet needs and re-enact a closure to satisfy them.

Psychodrama Re-enactment

For those readers that are unfamiliar with psychodrama techniques, our work is performed in a group setting with various members asked to role-play the characters identified in the re-enactment. In Jane's case, she had chosen several group members for various parts.

Jane told the group members of her intense longing to discover the identity of her "birth mother" and of her wish to finally meet her. She began to imagine going to the adoption agency and demanding to know the identity of her birth mother. She challenged the employee to reveal her mother's identity and the woman reluctantly gave Jane the information.

Jane then came face to face with her birth mother (a group member) who then leaned over and kissed Jane's cheek. After Jane finished role-playing her surplus reality, she reported to the group she felt better, calmer and left feeling happy. We facilitated Jane's psychodrama work so that she would physically experience being touched, hugged, and kissed by the group member she selected to role-play her birth mother. Thus, a new positive kinesthetic memory was created.

Three months after this work, Jane called us to report that she had actually decided to go to the adoption center. And just as she had role-played herself in the psychodrama workshop three months earlier, Jane confronted the employee to release the information as to the identity of her real mother. A drive to complete the work that had started in a psychodrama is a common response of those who have experienced surplus realities. Often, what was initially just role-play becomes fully manifested in real life as it had for Jane.

Jane and her husband drove to the mountain village where the records had indicated her birth mother resided. They went to the local church and spoke with the priest who assisted them in finding her birth mother's house. Jane's mother answered her knock upon the door. However, unlike her role-play where Jane was able to easily experience the kiss of her mother, there was another daughter in the room, also named Jane who shouted: "My mother has no other daughter than me. Get out!"

Jane left the house and went back to the church, but not until she had been able to hug and be hugged by her real mother. At last, her wish had come true. The priest told her: "It is very unlikely that two young girls with the same first and last names would give birth to two baby girls on the same day in such a small village. Therefore I believe she really is your mother, but is afraid to say anything in front of her legitimate daughter..." Jane's mother felt guilt and shame for having had an illegitimate child and had never spoken about it to her family.

Rupert Sheldrake's (1995) theory of Morphic Resonance may indeed offer some insight as to how Jane, in reality, had actually found her mother and experienced a deep healing from the trauma of being born illegitimate and abandoned. In order to make Jane's healing clearer, we ask the reader to remember the first kiss Jane experienced during her psychodrama reenactment work. Sheldrake would say that "kiss" (the kinesthetic-based implanted memory from the psychodrama work) became the catalyst that connected her with the magnetic-like energy waves in the morphogenetic field and allowed Jane to locate her mother in real life and heal herself from years of abandonment, anxiety and nightmares (Sheldrake, 1995).

Let us remember that life is full of coincidences that we call serendipity, and a re-enactment is often important enough that people then "do something" creative and healing with them.

Voltaire has already written about this happy coincidence in the Seventeenth Century in his Persian tales, as had Horace Walpole (1717-1797). Both frequented the famous literary salon of Madam du Deffand and enjoyed the ancient tale The Three Princes of Serendip (1557) [Note: Serendip was the ancient name for Sri Lanka where the recent tsunami occurred].

In Serendip, according to Walpole (1754) "People were always making discoveries, by accident and sagacity, of things which they were not in quest of," but things that were useful for friends and people they knew.

The term "serendipity" which evolved from this ancient tale, was used by the scientist Walter B. Cannon (1945) to qualify "the happy faculty, or luck, of finding unforeseen evidence of one's ideas or, with surprise, coming upon new objects or relations which were not being sought" (Schutzenberger, 2002).

Another example of "serendip" is Fleming's accidental discovery of penicillin from his observation of the mold he noticed in an unemptied wastepaper basket. Moreover, "serendipity" differs from Jung's "synchronicity" because you not only find things by surprise, but do something with them.

These coincidences, such as Jane experienced, are not really coincidences, if you look closely at them. They can even be found in nearly all recent scientific studies, and they can be found in the transgenerational and intergenerational research we do concerning the hidden meaning and relationship of filial bonds, family secrets, life incidents and accidents. Thus serendipity is at work even in medical discoveries.

Serendipity being present, the following discovery was made the same year in three different countries by people not knowing each other and under different terms! David Preston, in London is responsible for the anismus term. Pierre Arhan, in Paris, called this abnormal functioning The Disobedient Sphincter Syndrome (Preston, 1985; Hero & Arhan et al, 1985). And Han Kuijpers (1985), in Holland, baptized the abnormality: Spastic Pelvic Floor Syndrome (Kuijpers, 1985).

We have often spoken of anismus in this book. People strain to defecate and at the same time squeeze their anus, in order to not defecate. This is clearly an evidence of split personality, with one part of the personality fighting the other as if in a double-bind, and the body is the battlefield.

To conclude, we can say that in the long run, humans are quite a bit less free than we thought we were. However, we can recapture our liberty and stop the repetitions of traumas and transgenerational somatization if we notice the mold which has formed on the discarded event. By grabbing onto these old relational coincidences in their original context and in all their complexity, we can make use of the mold to heal ourselves and our loved ones.

We can begin to courageously remember the original past event in all its horror, and feel the feeling that we or our ancestor(s) needed to feel then. If we take the family secret "out of the closet," and give it some air, the mold can actually be transformed into penicillin.

In effect, as clinicians, this is how we are helping our patients find their healing potential.

We can imagine how fast the wound would have healed if we or our abused parent or grandparent had said what they needed to say then to their abuser, how their grief would have been washed away if only they cried instead of suffering in silence, and how the old hurts would have then left only sad memories but not unfelt emotional pain. By revealing the truth of these once secretive events, we release the need for the repressed emotional pain to manifest as a somatization in future generations' dis-eases.

It is possible to then finally live our lives, and not those of our parents and grandparents, or their loved ones who died tragically or behaved sexually, politically, or ethically in a manner that was socially unmentionable, unspeakable or unthinkable.

Psychodrama re-enactment actually creates a new surplus reality which replaces the memory that was "buried alive" without being resolved. We can imagine a new and completed version of the original trauma where painful emotional feelings finally get expressed and are no longer a secret chill inside one's bones, waiting only to be born again in these children's bodies. We can stop the transgenerational transmission of pain by telling and sharing the secrets, re-living and releasing the pain, thus bringing this unfinished business to a close.

Conclusion

The unconscious mind has a good memory, and our bodies record all the shocks they receive: the scars of the whip, the physical falls, the bodily accidents, the psychological shocks.

Traumas live long, often much longer than the person lives. Unresolved traumas live longer in the family tree if there has been no bereavement. If the traumatized person has not been able to talk about them, digest them or recover from them in his or her own lifetime, they remain, like unfinished, interrupted tasks, and often, much worse, are buried alive as hidden unhealed wounds.

Here we refer to the work of Kurt Lewin (1936) and his student Bluma Zeigarnik, which has become a classic in Gestalt theory and in group dynamics. What we call the Zeigarnik Effect concerns unaccomplished tasks and how they persist in our memory (Zeigarnik, 1927). We apply this term to "brooding over" bereavement that was left unfinished during the maturation process, various losses and serious traumas (Lewin, 1936).

What has not been accomplished and completed in its own time remains in memory. We brood for a long time, over years, and even generations. We turn over and over these things that tap on the system and wear us down. They correspond to the many physical wounds that have remained open and infected, incapable of healing over, and these wounds are thus transmitted in the heritage we hand down to our descendants.

In this book, we have tried to show that family secrets are noxious for descendants of victims of physical, psychic or sexual traumas, even if these traumas occurred a long time ago in the past.

This is particularly evident in the first and second chapters of this book, where the stories have in common past sexual abuse in the lives of the mothers of the people who suffer from digestive disorders. What appeared remarkable to us, and deserving of detailed description, was that the descendents' physical problems were resistant to all treatment and intervention, although they themselves had not been abused.

In addition, we found it equally remarkable that these children recovered only if their mother, who had been sexually abused during her own childhood, finally decided to get help. When the victim who had been sexually abused during her childhood, decided to get help and name the pain experienced during the abuse, her child recovered immediately in most cases. Its as if the child's body told the parent's story. In a certain way, this is not surprising.

Indeed, children, particularly when they are young, are like sponges, soaking up everything in their environment regardless of whether things are said, or left unsaid and only experienced. And above all, in this latter case.

When things are not named, the child cannot express them in words, because consciously he is not informed about the traumas that have occurred. They remain unsaid or unspeakable.

Freud did not speak about the unconscious in the present tense, but in the past. He used the word *unbencuste,* which is a past participle. The only solution that remains for a child to express what he or she feels is to use his or her body. This is somatization in the full meaning of the word (Freud, 1913).

In the first two chapters, we showed that shedding light on the parent's history of sexual abuse clearly had a positive and healing impact on the majority of children suffering in their digestive tracts. In these cases, the possibility of false memories or fantasies, which we raised with regards to the Oedipus Complex, is not the answer.

Quite simply because once the parent-victim spoke of their own hidden abuse, her child began to recover, and often that occurred even though the mother never spoke of her history to the child just the doctor or therapist. This book reveals a serious problem, namely that all traumas which are not worked through or healed in the original victim will in one way or another be transmitted to his or her descendents.

We tried to avoid a certain number of traps while writing this book. In particular, we do not pretend to have written a work of science. This book is full of anecdotes that all point the cause of physical gastrointestinal pain in the same direction: the transmission of a parents' traumatic unsaid information to a painful somatization in the child.

But science cannot be reduced to anecdotes. All science is made up of measurements, and to measure, one needs a lot of cases to consider. It is therefore necessary to reduce the ill subjects to objects of scientific measurement in order to count them and come up with a statistic. We have not done that here, for obvious reasons of methodology.

How could we scientifically show that the sexual abuse of a woman, silenced and unshared with anyone, can have a noxious impact on descendants? It would be necessary to take a hundred or so women who have been sexually abused during their childhood, ones who know they had been abused, which goes against our hypothesis, and not bring them any psychotherapy support to help them resolve their suffering. Just wait until they have had children and then do an in-depth medical evaluation of the children's digestive system. This absurd demonstration shows how extremely difficult it could be to carry out such a research project. In all likelihood, this scientific study will never be done.

A scientifically acceptable alternative would consist of studying a number of control cases. It would be necessary in this case to gather together a rather considerable number of children suffering from functional digestive disorders that do not respond to any medical treatment or intervention. Here already we encounter a difficulty, which is to define what we could consider as "not responding to any treatment" and not resolved by a certain number of people involved, which also needs to be defined.

Once the group of children were gathered, it would be necessary to ask their parents questions about family histories of sexual abuse concerning the mothers, fathers and ancestors, hoping—which is completely illusory—to get frank and true responses concerning the presence of sexual abuse. It is easy to imagine the reaction of parents who come to consult for a problem of constipation, incontinence or abdominal pain in their children who find themselves asked if they had been sexually abused during their childhood!

Unable to use either of these methods, we are left to present a series of anecdotes that all point in the same direction and that, even if they cannot be generalized to the entire population, nevertheless allow us to develop a hypothesis: when a child does not respond to any form of treatment, it is useful to explore his or her family's history and search for unspoken and unresolved trauma.

The systemic family approach is well known to pediatricians and often—more and more often—parents take part in the child's treatment. Helping the parents release their secret pain often leads to the non-medical resolution of their child's problem.

We have tried to go further than the simple issue of the daily relationship between parents and children, to approach the parents' secret suffering in order to help the child.

The second trap we tried to avoid was to only discuss cases of sexual abuse, particularly in the parent's childhood not the child who was a patient. The subject itself creates storms, and much more considerable ones in Europe than in North America.

If we look closely at the nature of sexual abuse (which is another form of abuse of authority), it is nothing more than the most blatant demonstration of disrespect for a child. We thus tried to broaden this crime to the misuse of a child's body by an adult, for the adult's own sexual needs. Thus, we went from physical abuse to symbolic abuse, forms of abuse which are very numerous and certainly very unclear and experienced as such by the mothers when they themselves were children and who are only now able to express their emotional pain since they have become adults and parents themselves. Thus, we also attempted to discuss symbolic abuse, which represents any invasion of a child's body with an attitude of use other than goodwill. We also tried to move away from the idea of sexuality to arrive at this idea that a child's body is not the parent's, nor is the child a clone of his or her parents, but a separate being, one whose integrity is to be fully respected. If it is not, there will be a trauma that will be somatized and transmitted to their future children if their emotional pain is not released.

The third trap we tried to avoid was that of intellectualization. The Cycle of Abuse is often translated by a phrase such as "better to have known unhappiness than unknown happiness," which leads innumerable victims of sexual abuse and other traumatisms into a "familiar" process of re-victimization of the same nature simply because it is a family repetition-compulsion.

This was the case of a young woman whose father was alcoholic and beat her. She married an alcoholic who beat her, whom she left for an alcoholic who did not beat her, whom she left for an ex-alcoholic who did not beat her, obviously gradually letting go of her familiar pattern.

Repetition-compulsion is a powerful indicator that the adult has indeed not emotionally left her childhood but it trying to reconstitute a more adequate childhood than the one she experienced which often forces or leads a person to continually go through the same noxious process hoping to act out a resolution.

But understanding, *really* understanding, is a particularly avoidant defense mechanism, especially if the person to whom the comprehension mechanisms are addressed confirms that he or she has been correctly heard and understood. In this way, understanding helps the victim dodge all the surrounding emotions.

It would therefore have been very tempting for us to reconstitute a family history of traumatisms and exclude all forms of interpretation of interpersonal relations. So, in the story of the impaled young woman, the fact that we knew of three generations of women before her who had been raped at the same age at which she impaled herself, would not have been enough. Neither our understanding of this history nor hers would have been enough in itself to help her. In fact, here and now, to speak as Gestalt practitioners do, this young woman had introjected her family secrets back into her dysfunctional parental family environment. There was the beginning of an incestuous relationship with her brother, but all of that was a symptom of the weight of the history of sexual abuse experienced by her mother, grandmother and great-grandmother. So therefore, there was emotional release work to be done not just with her mother but in her real life, even though the girl's current physical injury was in part programmed by the history of her ancestors.

The way some of the subjects described in this book healed rapidly after their mother's secret or unrecognized traumatisms were revealed to us can be explained by a more general process that applies beyond pathologies associated with sexual abuse or defecation disorders.

All children feel maternal anxiety, they can physically feel their mother's depression, or parental relationship dysfunction. As this negative feeling in the mother also keeps the child from feeling good about himself, helping the mother reveals what troubles her and, if possible, relieves her pain, automatically relieving the child. The result is that the child becomes capable of overcoming the odious problem that made his life miserable as long as his mother kept it as a secret within her.

When mothers feel better, their children feel better, and vice versa. All pediatricians know that, but generally they are left alone to ponder the issue and find the source of the problem to resolve it efficiently.

The children described in this book were not all cured. This leads us to introduce an important remark, which is that simply asking the questions is not enough.

To say that there was abuse does not automatically correct the mother's unconscious suffering linked to this abuse. That alone does not heal, but the admission of it does provide some relief. Emotional release through psychotherapy is therefore necessary.

It is therefore essential to state that the approach to this general problem cannot be simplistic, based on a simple link between cause and effect.

We conclude, on the other hand, that the stories told in this book are very good examples of what is now known as the Anniversary Syndrome. This syndrome has been repeatedly reported as explanations of psychological and psychiatric problems when abuse or trauma can be found in an earlier generation.

The step further we have taken here is to show that these

secret problems become bodily dysfunctions not just in the adult victims themselves, but in their children.

We do not know if the dysfunction can also be organic. The symptoms the patients in this book suffered from are mostly functional.

There is a lot of confusion both in the minds of patients and doctors, who equate imaginary illnesses with functional problems. We did not talk about imaginary illnesses. The patients described in this book suffered, for the most part, from problems of constipation, diarrhea, abdominal pain, anal incontinence, whose causes were not in sick organs which would be easily detectable with radiological and laboratory tests. Healthy organs do not change the fact that their problems were very real and measurable by all the functional tests we have available to us in modern medicine. In other words, there were no lesions. These anatomical structures functioned abnormally. On the other hand, these children's bodies were speaking out their unspoken pain and, mostly, the unspoken pain experienced by their mothers in their own childhood.

Even if we cannot claim to have scientifically proven that all unresolved trauma in one generation is transmitted to the next generation, often in the body more than in the mind, the fact remains that this transmission from parent to child has been described and proven scientifically, on a psychological and psychiatric level, by the American author, Josephine Hilgard (Hilgard, 1989, 1963, 1953).

In general, analysts claim that words are the ultimate response and talking about trauma is enough. They may be right, but too often, when words contradict the body, certain people will deny or avoid the bodily reality and emphasize the explanation there by avoiding the feelings and words, which is often an error of a psychotic nature.

Let us recall here Leon Festinger's theory of "cognitive dissonance," which shows that one of the ways to resolve the discomfort of a contradiction is to underestimate it or, quite simply, not see it, thereby unconsciously reducing its effect (Festinger, 1957). As long as there is incongruence between one's "body talk" & spoken word, there is room for intellectual elaboration until the disagreement disappears. Therefore, there is not antagonism between thought and the body, but a non-coordination.

It would be presumptuous to think that life began with us. We are heirs to our ancestors' history. What is transmitted from generation to generation is not only our flesh and genes. The stories told here provide ample demonstration that we are part of a humanity in the becoming, a "going-becoming" (*allant-devenant*) as Françoise Dolto said (Dolto, 1993).

This book is not meant to be a full-frontal attack against parents. Poor parents, they did what they could; taking into consideration the traumas they themselves experienced and the knowledge—or lack of knowledge—they had at the time. What we say is not to lay guilt on parents; on the contrary, it's to say that we have all done as much or as little as we were capable of doing for our children.

To respond in advance to people who, despite everything, may become annoyed, both of us, as authors of this book, are over sixty years old, we both have children and grandchildren, and we both have made mistakes with them.

And we are both convinced that the etymological meaning

of the word "sin" in Hebrew is very appropriate, because it simply means: to miss the target! Remember, too, that Oedipus punished himself for not having seen things in time! When he saw, he was pardoned...

But we are all heirs to our ancestors' pain. As the Bible says, the sins of the father are rested in the children (Paraphrased) (Deut. 28:58, *The Holy Bible* RSV, (1966). We have written more about the sins against the mother.

They bequeathed us chromosomes, but also habits and customs, beliefs and behavior patterns. And sometimes, it occurs that these behavior patterns are translated into symptoms, where our bodies become the spokesperson for our ancestors' pain.

Glossary

Anismus: A recto-anal dysfunction. When a normal person strains to defecate, his anus relaxes completely to allow the stool to pass easily. When there is anismus, instead of relaxing, the anus can even contract. This anomaly forces the subject to strain much harder. "It doesn't want to go through," patients say, "but I feel like I have to keep going." So they make great efforts, which can much later lead them to have all kinds of problems related to lowering organs. Even if the presence of anismus does not necessarily mean that there has been sexual abuse in the past, it has nevertheless been proven that this traumatism can be found ten times more often in the pasts of subjects with anismus.

Anorectal manometry: A technique used to measure pressure in the anus and the rectum. A small plastic catheter, barely bigger than a thermometer, is introduced into the rectum. It contains several tubes tied together that allows one to record pressure at different levels.

Biofeedback: A physiotherapy technique that allows one to show a patient the effect the contraction or relaxation of a muscle has on an electronic apparatus, either through a sound that becomes higher, or for children a small person climbing stairs instead of going down, or quite simply electronically, through the traces of a needle, which rises when there is a contraction and descends when there is relaxation. This technique is frequently used in medical circles and among physiotherapists with varying results, but often with success.

Catharsis: Taken from Greek, this term was introduced by Joseph Breuer, Sigmund Freud's teacher, to designate the release of affect or emotions during hypnosis. Freud broadened this term to cover emotional expression during psychoanalysis, completing it with a longer, restructuring working through of emotions using dreams, faulty acts and relapses. He spoke about a talking cure before creating the term psychoanalysis and renouncing catharsis, which he was wary of because its effects were not always lasting.

Colectomy: Ablation of part of the colon.

Colonoscopy: Technique for inspecting the colon by introducing an endoscope, which is an articulated optical apparatus, made up of tens of thousands of minuscule optic fibers.

Crohn's disease: An inflammatory disease of the intestine, for which no cause of infection has been found with enough serious proof that upheld the test of time. It carries the name of Dr. Burril Crohn, an American physician who described it in 1931. In fact, it had already been described in 1916 by an obscure Scottish doctor name Kennedy Dalziel, who had correctly recognized that this disease differed from tuberculosis, even if under the microscope some anomalies were similar. For a long time, this disease was considered to be a pathology that only touched the small intestine, until 1953 when a surgeon from Liverpool named Wells showed proof of the existence of Crohn's disease in the large intestine. North America was slower than Europe in adopting this concept, and it was only in 1968 that Crohn's disease was recognized throughout the world as a disease of the whole body, with predominance in the digestive tract, and particularly in the lower part of the small intestine. But, lesions have been described as existing elsewhere, from the mouth to the anus, and its existence has even been recognized outside the digestive tract: on the skin, calves, vulva, etc.

The cardinal symptoms of this disease are abdominal pains, with diarrhea and febricula. Its complications are obstructive or take the form of fistula, and it seems that on this basis there are two families of patients. The major complications are obstructions, perforations and infections, hemorrhage and, more rarely, cancerization. Subjects who suffer from the disease lose proteins and nutrients, and lose weight or have retarded growth.

We do not know the cause of the disease. It seems likely that immunity disorders are at play, notable weakened immunity or auto-immunity, where the subject attacks himself. Even if the concept is not well accepted, there is a lot of psychopathology linked to this disease, and it predated the disease itself, which is a strong argument against the idea that it merely reflects the large morbidity of this pathology. The subjects who suffer from Crohn's disease are often depressed and have a predilection for situations of great control over themselves and over others. Case-control studies have shown that subjects suffering from Crohn's disease had not gone through their adolescent crises, had not cut the umbilical cord with their parents, or symbolic substitutes.

Work remains to be done in finding treatment for Crohn's disease. Surgery is reserved strictly for complications and has absolutely no curative value; it is only palliative when there are complications. Treatment through medication is effective, but one should not forget that the placebo effect works in 40% of cases.

Dissociation: A psychological process that allows a subject to distance himself from a reality that is too harsh to accept. The traumatized subject splits into a wounded, handicapped part and another, healthier part, which becomes an observer of the traumatized subject. This second part can grow and become "resilient," particularly when the subject in this post-traumatic stress syndrome situation can find a supportive environment. The weakness of this situation is that it is based on a weak spot, a split of the subject into two unintegrated parts. This split can be observed in many ways: between intelligence, the psyche and the body; between intelligence and emotions; between masculine and feminine, etc.

Dissociation can also be induced, in an attempt to explore the wounded part; this is one of the first steps in the hypnotic process.

Diverticulitis: An inflammation that occurs when a small hernia of the colon is perforated from too much internal pressure. In this case, direct contact occurs between the stool found inside the large intestine and the peritoneum, leading to peritonitis, which can be deadly if it is neglected. Diverticulosis, on the other hand, is omnipresent in the Western world, with a prevalence of about ten percent per decade of age: one person out of two at the age of fifty, and everyone has it at a hundred…

Ericksonian hypnosis: Still referred to as "hypnosis without hypnosis." Generally speaking, classical hypnosis, inherited from the nineteenth century and using hypnotic induction based on stereotypical techniques that tend to be authoritative and intrusive, is contrasted with Ericksonian hypnosis, which is named after the American psychiatrist Milton H. Erickson (1901-1980), who used it frequently in his practice. He developed an approach centered on the specificities of each individual. This type of hypnosis is actually used by the majority of caregivers, without their knowledge. It is essentially based on a vast array of communication techniques, non-verbal language, capturing all the help-seeking person's body messages, from humor, through confusion, paradoxical injunction and therapeutic double binds. For Erickson, the hypnotic experience is banal and daily for each of us, and is, above all, a learning situation. This learning situation consists, for each patient, of using his or her resistance to change to better overcome it through an approach akin to "mental judo." Due to his inventiveness and the wealth of his essentially clinical approach, Milton H. Erickson's influence reached far beyond the field of hypnosis. Even if the goal of Ericksonian hypnosis is not to heal, but to lead the subject to find his or her capacity for transformation, elements of a psychoanalytical kind of transfer also come into play, as in all human relations, although ideally this does not occur without the caregiver's knowledge.

Fecal Impaction: Accumulation of extremely hard fecal matter in the rectum, which takes on such a large form that it becomes impossible to pass the stool through the anus. Liquid stools move around the obstacle and the subject, incapable of holding them in, leaks them uncontrollably.

Genogram: A family tree covering three generations, containing certain life facts, highlighting the links among children, parents and grandparents. This tool is mostly used in systemic family therapy to treat the pathological family system.

Genosociogram: A family tree encompassing five to seven generations, showing dates (marriages, births, deaths) and important facts in the history of the family (level of studies, profession, separations, remarriages, illnesses and accidents, moves, uprooting, etc., including wars, traumas, fires and disasters), as well as the affective (sociometric) bonds between the individuals. This technique was developed by Anne Ancelin Schützenberger, based on the work of J.L. Moreno on the "social atom", and on broadening genodrama.

Hirschsprung's Disease: A congenital disease that causes constipation. Only surgery can save these patients. Although the disorder is not very widespread, the patient could spend his entire life constipated, from birth. Yet, certain children die from it if they are not operated on.

Irritable Bowel Syndrome (IBS): A very frequent disorder found in one person out of five. Three women out of four suffer from it, except in India, where men more frequently have this problem. There are several forms of Irritable Bowel Syndrome: the form characterized by constipation, the one characterized by diarrhea, and the one that alternates the two problems. Those suffering from IBS have abdominal pain that diminishes when they have a bowel movement. The syndrome is also accompanied by bowel movement frequency and stool consistency changes. These symptoms are what are known as the Rome II Diagnostic Criteria (name after the city where the experts gathered).

It is important to note that the presence of blood in stools, recent changes in the frequency or appearance of stools, loss of weight, and fever are not part of these criteria, and are considered to be "alarm signals," which should be looked into to screen for possible illness.

Many labels have been given to this disorder. English speakers refer to "irritable bowel," but others talk about "irritable stomach," because the subjects who suffer from it also have troubles in the esophagus, with the acid reflux, a burning liquid in the mouth, and heaviness with the stomach as well as troubles in the small intestine. Certain French-speaking authors talk about "unhappy colitis," in a very clear, and exact, reference to the associated psychosomatic problem, but using poor terminology, because there is no inflammation, and therefore no "-itis." Others will use the word "spasmophilia," a term that is poorly accepted by the medical community, even if it has been demonstrated that a third of IBS sufferers have bronchial spasms, when they are stimulated in the lab to see if they tend to have asthma. IBS sufferers have all kinds of symptoms, all of which are functional, ranging from the head to the feet, in all the systems, the most frequent being headaches and heart palpitations, as well as backaches without their being and hernia in the spinal column.

Proctoscopy: Examination of the rectum with a 10-inch rigid tube with a light at the end. Before the use of colonoscopes, this was the only instrument available to visually examine the large intestine. It remains an indispensable tool, although not very "fashionable," except among surgeons specialized in diseases of the colon and the rectum; they use it to see the lesions in the lower part of the rectum.

Psychodrama: A technique perfected by J.L. Moreno, which consists of playing out scenes of one's own past, present and future, and even of one's own imagination, instead of only talking about them. It involves the body experience and the relationship to others.

Four major techniques are often used (interested readers can find out more in Anne Ancelin Schutzenberger's *Le Psychodrame*, Paris, Payot, 2003, which contains around one hundred techniques, an extensive glossary and a large bibliography).

Role Reversal. Each person takes the role and the place of the person (parent, boss, employee, teacher, brother, sister, child, etc.), or even the animal or object that is causing difficulties, and then expresses himself "for the other," which opens the way to much understanding.

Projection into the future. We play out the situation as we imagine it will be in five or ten years, exploring things psycho-dramatically.

Surplus reality. For a difficult life situation (for example, saying goodbye in time to a dying parent one was not able to see again, or, for an orphan, having a living father), one acts "as if" one could go back in time and have the opportunity to express one's feelings, to experience tenderness, which often allows the individual to leave behind his suffering.

Role playing. Application of psychodrama in education, in businesses, in family therapy.

Recto-anal inhibitory reflex: When the rectum is distended, for example by a small balloon that is inserted and inflated, the anus relaxes, and this relaxation can be recorded by anorectal manometry. This reflex is always absent with Hirschsprung's Disease. But lab errors do occur, which leads us to say that if the reflex is recorded, there is no chance of Hirschsprung's Disease, but if it is not found, one should think of it.

Replacement child: A child conceived or born to replace a deceased loved one, often a child who had died prematurely, but sometimes also a parent or grandparent. This was the case with Dali, and also with Van Gogh, who was born one year after the death of his brother Vincent. According to André Green, a replacement child has a bereaving mother, or one suffering from depression, that takes care of her child without ever really seeing him. Often, but not always, this child becomes schizophrenic or dies prematurely. Some children, on the other hand, are quite well seen and very animated, as is the case with "repairing" children.

Resistance to change: The work of the psycho-sociologist Kurt Lewin showed that change is not as simple as once thought: resistance to change develops (studied in group dynamics); but afterwards, one always finds a nearly stationary, not very stable, balance. Then, by studying all the forces at work one can find the force or tool that will engender a small transformation that will in turn determine other transformations.

We confront this resistance to change every time we confront a change of lifestyle, of food or other habits, of belief, of patterns of thought, of action, of breathing, of posture, which explains why brutal, rapid change causes the organism, or the family or the society to react, and that real change often takes time, or needs to be reinforced.

References

Abraham, Nicolas and Maria Torok. (1978). *L'Ecorce et le noyau.* Paris: Aubier Flammarion. (Revised Edition, 1987). Edited and translated by Nicolas Rand, *The Shell and the Kernel.* Chicago and London: Chicago University Press, 1994.

Ancelin Schutzenberger, Anne, Bissone Jaufroy, Evelyne (2005). *Sortia du Devil et de toutes pertes (Getting out of bereavement and all losses).* Paris: France: Payot.

Ancelin Schützenberger, Anne. (2003). *Aïe, mes aïeux!* 17th edition. 2003. Paris: Desclée de Brower/La Méridienne, 1998. Translated by Anne Trager, *The Ancestor Syndrome.* London and New York: Routledge.

Ancelin Schützenberger, Anne. (2003). "Les secrets de famille, les non-dits et le syndrome d'anniversaire," in J. Aïn (ed.), *Transmissions, liens et filiations. Secrets et repetitions,* 149-171. Toulouse: Erès.

Ancelin Schützenberger, Anne. (2003). "Contribution à une histoire de vie," in V. de Gauléjac (ed.), *Histoire de vie et choix théoriques. Femmes et sciences socials.* Paris: L'Harmattan.

Ancelin Schützenberger, Anne. (2003). "C'est le corps qui triomphe," in W. Barral, *Françoise Dolto, c'est la parole qui fait vivre. Une théorie corporelle du langage,* 2e edition. Paris: Gallimard.

Ancelin Schutzenberger, Anne. (2003). *Le Psychodrame.* Paris: Petite Biliotheque Payot.

Ancelin Schützenberger, Anne. (1996). "La sérendipité," in *Hommage au Doyen Weiss.* Nice: Publications de la Faculté des Lettres. *Arts et sciences humaines de Nice,* no. 2, 60-81.

Ancelin Schützenberger, Anne. (1985). *Vouloir guérir. L'aide au malade atteint d'un cancer.* Paris: Desclée de Brower.

Ancelin Schützenberger, Anne. (1978). *Contribution à l'étude de la communication non verbale.* Paris: Université de Lille-III/Librairie Champion.

Anzieu, Didier. (1987). "Les signifiants formels et le moi-peau," in Didier Anzieu (ed.), *Les Enveloppes psychiques.* Paris: Dunod.

Badgley, R. (1984). *Sexual Offenses Against Children. The Badgley Report.* Donald Mcdonald Law and Government Division, Research Branch. Ottawa, Canada: Librairy of Parliament.

Barral, Willy (ed.). (2003). Françoise Dolto, c'est la parole qui fait vivre. Une théorie corporelle du langage, 2nd edition. Paris: Gallimard.

Bateson, Gregory. (1972). *Steps to an Ecology of Mind.* New York: Dutton.

Bateson, Gregory, Don Jackson and J. Haley. 1956. "Toward a Theory of Schizophrenia," *Behavior Scientist* 1: 251-264.

Birdwhistell, Ray L. (1970). *Kinesics and Context. Essays on Body Motion Communication.* University of Philadelphia Press.

Bouchoucha, M., Devroede, G., Arhan, P., Strom, B., Weber, J., Cugnenc, P. H., & Denis, P., Barbier, J. P. (1992). "What is the meaning of colorectal transit time measurement?" *Diseases of Colon and Rectum,* 35 (8): 773-783.

Boszormenyi-Nagy, Ivan & Spark, G. M. (1973). *Invisible Loyalties.* New York: Harper & Row.

Bowen, Murray. (1978). *Family Therapy in Clinical Practice.* New York: Jason Aronson.

Bowen, Murray. (1978). *La differentiation du soi.* Paris: ESF. Translated 1984.

Bryant, Richard (2005). Post traumatic stress disorder unit, University of New South Wales, quoted from American Online News (Internet), January 2, 2005.

Cannon, Walter Bradford. (1945). *The Way of an Investigator.* New York: Norton.

Charron, R. (1993). "The narrative road to empathy," in H. Spiro, *Empathy and the Medical Profession. Beyond Pills and the Scalpel,* p. 147-159. New Haven: Yale University Press.

Charron R., Greene M., & Adelman R. (1994). "Multidimensional interaction analysis. A collaborative approach to the study of medical discourse", *Social Science and Medicine,* 39: 955-965.

Corneau, Guy. (1989). Père manquant, fils manqué. Que sont les hommes devenus? Paris: Editions de l'Homme. Translated by Larry Shouldice, Absent Fathers, Lost Sons: The Search for Masculine Identity, Boston: Shambhala, 1991.

Cyrulnik, Boris. (2002). *Le Murmure des fantômes.* Paris: Odile Jacob. Translated by Marjolijn de Jager, *Whispering of Ghosts,* New York: Other Press, 2004.

Cyrulnik, Boris, (1999). *Un merveilleux Malheur.* Paris: Odile Jacob.

Dejours, C. (2003). Le Corps, d'abord. Corps biologique, corps érotique et sens moral. Paris: Payot.

Devroede, Ghislain. (2002). *Ce que les maux de ventre dissent de notre passé.* Paris: Payot, and 2003. Paris: Petite Biliothèque Payot.

Devroede, Ghislain (2000). "Early life abuses in the past history of patients with gastrointestinal tract and pelvic floor dysfunction," chapter X in E. A. Mayer, C.B. Saper (eds.), *The Biological Basis for Mind-Body Interactions,* coll. "Progress in Brain Research", vol. 122, p. 131-155. Amsterdam, Lausanne, New York, Oxford, Singapour, Tokyo: Elsevier Science BW.

Devroede, Ghislain. (1995). "Psychophysiological considerations in subjects with chronic idiopathic constipation," chapter XXII in S. D. Wexner, D.C.C. Barolot (ed.), *Constipation, Etiology, Evaluation and Management,* 103-134. Oxford: Butterworth Heinemann.

Devroede, Ghislain. (1994). "Constipation," chapter XXXVII in D. Kumar, D.L. Wingate (ed.), *An Illustrated Guide to Gastrointestinal Motility,* 2e edition, p. 595-654. Edinburgh: Churchill Livingstone.

Devroede, Ghislain. (1993). "Radiopaque marker measurement of colorectal transit," in M. M. Schuster (ed.), *Atlas of Gastrointestinal Motility in Health and Disease,* 57-75. Baltimore: Williams & Wilkins.

Devroede, Ghislain. (1992). "Constipation: a sign of a disease to be treated surgically, or a symptom to be deciphered as non verbal communication?" *J. Clin. Gastroenterology,* 15 (3): 189-191.

Dickinson, Anthony (1980). *Comtemporary Animal Learning Theory.* Cambridge University Press: New York.

Dolto, Françoise. (1993). *Tu as choisi de naître, Parler vrai, N'ayez pas peur.* Videos by E. Coronel and A. de Mezamat. Paris: Editions Montparnasse/Abacaris Films.

Dolto, Françoise. (1969). *Au jeu du désir. Essais cliniques.* Paris: Seuil.

Dolto, Françoise. (1988). *Inconscient et Destin.* Paris: Seuil.

Dolto, Françoise. (1984). *L'Image inconsciente du corps.* Paris: Seuil.

Dolto, Françoise & Ariès, P. (1984). "L'enfant isolé des adultes," *L'Enfant d'abord,* no. 92, December.

Drossman, D. A., Corazziari, E., Talley, N. J., Thompson, W. G., & Whitehead, W. E. (1999). "Rome II. A multinational consensus document on functional gastrointestinal disorders," *Gut.*, 45 (suppl II): 1-81.

Drossman, D. A., Leserman, J., Nachman, G., Li, Z. M., Gluck, H., Toomey T. C., & Mitchell C. M. (1990). "Sexual and physical abuse in women with functional or organic gastrointestinal disorders," *Ann. Int. Med.*, 113: 828-833.

Drossman, D. A., McKee, D. C., Sandler, R. S., Mitchell, C. M., Cramer, E. M., Lowman, B. C., & Burger, A. L. (1988). "Psychosocial factors in the Irritable Bowel Syndrome. A multivariate study of patients and non patients with Irritable Bowel Syndrome," *Gastroenterology*, 95 (3): 701-708.

Drossman, D. A., Talley, N. J., Leserman, J., Olden, K. W., & Barreiro M. A. (1995). "Sexual and physical abuse and gastrointestinal illness. Review and recommendations," *Ann. Int. Med.*, 123: 782-794.

Dumas, Didier. (2001). *La Bible et ses fantômes.* Paris: Desclée de Brouwer.

Dumas, Didier. (1999). Sans père et sans parole. La place du père dans l'équilibre de l'enfant. Paris: Hachette Littératures.

Dumas, Didier. (2003). "L'image inconsciente du corps dans la mobilité corporelle et sexuelle de l'esprit," in Willy Barral (ed.), *Françoise Dolto, c'est la parole qui fait vivre. Une tthéorie corporelle du langage*, 2e ed. Paris: Gallimard.

Dumas, Didier. (1985). L'ange et le Fantôme. Introduction à la clinique de l'impensé généalogique. Paris: Minuit.

Feldman, P. C., Villanueva, S., & Lanne, V., Devroede, G. (1993). "Use of play with clay to treat children with intractable encopresis," *Journal of Paediatrics*, 122 (3): 483-487.

Festinger, Leon. (1957). *A Theory of Cognitive Dissonance.* Evanston: Roy Peterson.

Foely, Meraiah (2005). *Mom forced to choose sons during tsunami.* Internet news article Associated Press posted on American Online January 2, 2005.

Freud, Sigmund. (1913). Totem and Taboo, in The Standard Edition of the Complete Psychological Works of Sigmund Freud. New York: WW. Norton & Co., 1962.

Freud, Sigmund. (1923). The Ego and the Id, in The Standard Edition of the Complete Psychological Works of Sigmund Freud. New York: WW. Norton & Co., 1962.

Freud, Sigmund. (1919). The uncanny, in The Standard Edition of the Complete Psychological Works of Sigmund Freud. New York: WW. Norton & Co., 1962.

Freud, S. (1999/1907b). *Der Dichter und das Phantasieren.* In Gesammelte Werke. Frankfurt am Main: Fischer Verlag.

Freud, S. (1999/1900). *Die Traudetung.* In Gesammelte Werke. Chronologisch geordnet. Frankfurt am Main: Fischer Verlag.

Freud, S. (1999/1908). *Hysterische Phantasien und ihre Beziehung zur Bissexualitat.* In Gesammelte WErke. Chronologisch geordnet. Frankfurt am Main: Fischer Verlag.

Freud, S. (1999/1896). *Zur Atiologie der Hysterie.* In Gesammelte Werke. Chronologisch geordnet. Frankfurt am Main: Fischer Verlag.

Gauléjac, Vincent de. (1999). *L'Histoire en héritage.* Paris: Desclée de Brouwer.

Gauléjac, Vincent de. (1996). *Les Sources de la honte.* Paris: Desclée de Brouwer.

Gauléjac, Vincent de. (1987). *La Névrose de classe.* Paris: Hommes & Groupes.

Greene, M., Adelman, R., Freidmann, E., & Charron, R. (1994). "Older patient satisfaction with communication during initial medical encounter," *Social Science and Medicine*, 38: 1279-1288.

Guthrie, E., Creed, F., Dawson, D. M., & Torrensen, B. (1991). "A controlled trial of psychological treatment for the Irritable Bowel Syndrome," *Gastroenterology*, 100: 450-457.

Guthrie, E., Creed, F., & Whorwell, P. J. (1987). "Severe sexual dysfunction in women with the Irritable Bowel Syndrome: comparison with inflammatory bowel disease and duodenal ulceration," *British Medical journal. Clinical Research*, 295 (6598): 577-578.

Guy-Gillet, Geneviève. (1994). *La Blessure de Narcisse.* Paris: Albin Michel.

Harrus-Révidi, G. (2001). *Parents immatures et enfants-adultes.* Paris: Payot.

Hémond M., Bédard G., Bouchard H., Arhan P., Watier A., & Devroede G. (1995). "Step-by-step anorectal manometry: small balloon tube," in L.E. Smith (ed.), *Practical guide to Anorectal Testing*, 2nd edition, p. 101-141. New York, Tokyo: Igaku-Shoin.

Hero, M., Arhan, P., Devroede, G., Jehannin, B., Faverdin, C., Babin, C., Pellerin, D. (1985). "Measuring the anorectal angle," *Journal of Biomedical Engineering*, 7: 321-325.

Hilgard, Josephine R. (1989). "The anniversary syndrome as related to late-appearing mental illness in hospitalized patients," in A.L.S. Silver, ed. *Psychoanalysis and Psychosis.* Madison, Conn: International University Press.

Hilgard, Josephine R. (1963). "Parental loss by death in childhood as an etiological factor among schizophrenic and alcoholic patients compared with a non-patient community sample," *Journal of Nervous and Mental disease* 137: 14-28.

Hilgard, Josephine R. (1953). Anniversary reactions in

parents precipitated by children," *Psychiatry,* 16: 73-80.

Hilgard, Josephine & Newman, M. "Evidence for functional genesis in mental illness: schizophrenia, depressive psychoses and psychoneuroses," *J. Nerv. Mental Dis.,* 132(1): 3-16.

Holmes T., Rahe R. (1967). "The social readjustment rating scale," *Journal of Psychosomatic Research,* 11: 213-218.

Hugo, Victor (1862). *Les Miserables.* Library of Congress, Washington, D.C. (In complete works of Victor Hugo).

Jost, W. H., Schrank, B., Herold, A., & Lein, O. (1999). "Functional outlet obstruction: anismus, spastic pelvic floor syndrome, and dyscoordination of the voluntary sphincter muscles," *Scand J. Gastroenterology,* 5: 449-456.

Kaës, René (ed.). (2001). Transmission de la vie psychique entre générations. Paris: Dunod.

Klauser, A.G., Voderholzer, W.A., Heinrich, C.A., Schindlbeck N.E., Muller-Lissner S.A. (1990). "Behavioral modification of colonic function. Can constipation be learned?" *Digestive Diseases and Sciences,* 35 (10): 1271-1275.

Kubler-Ross, Elizabeth. (1969). *On Death and Dying.* NY: Touchstone (Simon & Schuster).

Kuijpers, H.C., & Bleijenbberg, G. (1985). "The spastic pelvic floor syndrome. A cause of constipation," *Dis. Colon Rectum,* 28: 669-672.

Lani, M. (1990). A la recherche…de la génération perdue. Histoire de tragédies "en" et "sans" famille. Paris: Hommes & Perspectives/Journal des Psychologues.

Laplante, Patrice (1660). The Couvade Syndrome: the biological, psychological, and social impact of pregnancy on the expectant father. *Can Fam Physican* (1991), 37: 1633-36.

Lattimore, Richard (1967/1906). *The Odyssey of Homer.*

Epic poetry, Greek, translated by Richard Lattimore. New York: HarperCollins

Leader, D. (2000). *Freud's Footnotes*. London: Faber & Faber.

Lebovici, S. (1995). "Surmoi II. Les développements post-freudiens," *Monographies de la Revue française de Psychanalyse*. Paris: PUF.

Lerner Goldhor, H. (1985). *The Dance of Anger*. New York: Harper.

Leroi, A. M., Bernier, C., Watier, A., Hémond, M., Goupil, G., Black, R., Denis P., & Devroede, G. (1995). "Prevalence of sexual abuse among patients with functional disorders of the lower intestinal tract," *International Journal of Colorectal Disease*, 10: 200-206.

Leroi, A. M., Berkelmans, I., Denis, P., Hémond, M., & Devroede, G. (1995). "Anismus as a marker of sexual abuse: consequences of sexual abuse on anorectal motility," *Digestive Diseases and Sciences*, 40 (7): 1411-1416.

Levy, R. L., Jones, K. R., Whitehead, W. E., Feld, S. I., Talley, N. J., & Corey, L.A. (2001). "Irritable Bowel Syndrome in twins: heredity and social learning both contribute to etiology," *Gastroenterology*, 121: 799-804.

Levy, R. L., Whitehead, W. E., von Korff, M. R., & Feld, A. D. (2000). "Intergenerational transmission of gastrointestinal illness behavior," *The American Journal of Gastroenterology*, 95(2): 451-456.

LeShan, Lawrence (1980). *You can fight for your life*. NY: M. Evans & Co.

Lewin, Kurt. (1936). *Principles of Topological Psychology*. Translated by Fritz Heider, Asstn. Professor, Dept. of Ed., Smith College & Grace M. Heider. (First Ed., Fourth Impression). New York, London: McGraw-Hill

Book Co., Inc.

McDougall, Joyce. (1995). The Many Faces of Eros: a psychoanalytical exploration of human sexuality. New York: WW Norton.

Malarewicz, Jacques-Antoine. (1990). *Cours d'hypnose clinique.* Paris: ESF.

Martelli, H., Faverdin, C., Devroede, G., Goulet, O., Jais, J. P., Hambourg, M., Besançon-Lecointe, I., & Arhan P. (1998). "Can functional constipation begin at birth?" *Gastroenterology International,* 11(1): 1-11.

Martelli, H., Devroede, G., Arhan, P., Duguay, C., Dornic, C., & Faverdin, C. (1978). "Some parameters of large bowel motility in normal man," *Gastroenterology,* 75: 612-618.

Martelli, H., Devroede, G., Arhan, P., & Duguay, C. (1978). "Mechanisms of idiopathic constipation: outlet obstruction," *Gastroenterology,* 75: p. 623-631.

May, R. (1973). *Le Désir d'être.* Paris: Epi.

May, Rollo. (1969). *Existential Psychology.* New York: Random House.

Mead, Margaret. (1969). "From intuition to analysis in communication research," *Semiotics,* 1 (1): 13-25.

Miller, Alice. (1981). *Prisoners of Childhood,* translated by Ruth Ward. New York: Basic Books, and 1990, *Drama of the Gifted Child.*

Moreno, Jacob Levy. (1987). The Essential Moreno: writings on Psychodrama, Group Method and Spontaneity. New York: Beacon House.

Nachin, Claude. (1993). Les Fantômes de l'âme. A propos des héritages psychiques. Paris: L'Harmattan.

Pennebaker, J. W., Kiecolt-Glaser, J. K., & Glaser, R. (1988). "Disclosure of traumas and immune function. Health implications for psychotherapy," *Journal of consulting and Clinical Psychology,* 56 (2): 239-245.

Preston, D. M., & Lennard-Jones, J. E. (1985). "Anismus in

chronic constipation," *Digestive Diseases and Sciences,* 30(5): 413-418.

Oxford English Dictionary (2002). (10th Revised Ed.).UK: Oxford University Press

Rappaport, M. Summer (2003). "Des mots pour guérir les maux," *McGill News-Alumni quarterly.* Québec (Canada).

Ricoeur, Paul. (1990). *Soi-même comme un autre.* Paris: Seuil. Translated by Kathleen Blamey, (1992). *Oneself as another.* Chicago: Chicago University Press.

Rosenblatt, Jay S., & Snowdon, Charles T. (1996). *Parental Care evolution, mechanisms, and adaptive significance.* Academic Press, San Diego.

Roustang, François. (1994). *Qu'est-ce que l'hypnose?* Paris: Minuit.

Sami-Ali. (1998). Corps réel, corps imaginaire. Pour une épistémologie du somatique, 2nd edition. Paris: Dunod.

Servan-Schreiber, David. (2003). Guérir le stress, l'anxiété, la dépression sans médicament ni psychanalyse. Paris: Robert Laffont. Translated, The instinct to heal: curing stress, anxiety and depression without drugs and without talk therapy. Emmaus, Pa: Rodale, 2004.

Sheldrake, Rupert (1995). *The presence of the past: morphic resonance and the habits of nature.* (Reprint Ed.). Rochester, VT: Inner Traditions.

Spitz, René. (1969). *De la naissance à la parole.* Paris: PUF.

Scrignar, Chester B. (1984). *Post Traumatic Stress Disorder: Diagnosis, Treatment, and Legal Issues.* (Third Edition). Praeger Publishers, Westport, CT.

Stern, D. N. (1985). The interpersonal World of the Infant. A View from Psychoanalysis and Developmental Psychology. New York: Basic Books.

Stoddart, Michael D. (1990). *The Scented Ape.* The biology and culture of human odour. Cambridge Press

University, New York.

Teachworth, Anne (2001). Tears of Strength. *The Times Picayune*, September 20, 2001; New Orleans.

The Holy Bible (1966). (RSV) (Catholic Edition). Ignatius Press: San Francisco.

Tisseron, Serge. (1999). Nos secrets de famille. Histoire et mode d'emploi. Paris: Ramsay.

Tisseron, Serge. (1985). *Tintin chez le psychanalyste.* Paris: Aubier-Archimbaud.

Trevarthen, C. (1997). "Les racines du langage avant la parole," *Devenir,* vol. III, no. 3.

Verduron, A., Devroede, G., Bouchoucha, M., Arhan P., Schang, J. C., Poisson, J., Hémond, M., & Hébert, M. (1988). "Megarectum," *Digestive Diseases and Sciences*, 33(9): 1164-1174.

Vigouroux, Françoise. (1993). *Le Secret de famille.* Paris: PUF.

Wald, A., Hinds, J. P., & Camana, B. J. (1989). "Psychological and physiological characteristics of patients with severe idiopathic constipation," *Gastroenterology,* 97: 932-937.

Walker, E. A *et. al.* (1992). "Dissociation in women with chronic pelvic pain," *American Journal of Psychiatry,* 149(4): 534-537.

Walpole, Horace (1754). Coined the term *Serendipity.* Based upon the ancient tale: *The Three Princes of Serendip* (1557). Venice, Italy: Published by Michael Tramezzzino.

Watier, A., Feldman, P., Martelli, H., Arhan, P., & Devroede, G. (1995). "Hirschsprung's Disease," in W.B. Haurbrich, F. Schaffner (eds.), *Bockus Gastroenterology,* 5th ed. W. J. Snape.

Watzlawick, P., & Beavin, J. (1969). "Pragmatics of human communication: a study of interactional patterns, pathologies and paradoxes." New York: Norton.

Welgan, P., Meshkinpour, H., & Beeler, M. (1988). "Effect of anger on colon motor and myoelectric activity in Irritable Bowel Syndrome," *Gastroenterology*, 94: 1150-1156.

Welgan, P., Meshkinpour, H., & Ma, L. (2000). "Role of anger in antral motor activity in Irritable Bowel Syndrome," *Digestive Diseases and Sciences*, 45 (2): 248-251.

Whorwell, P. J., Prior, A., & Colgan, S. M. (1987). "Hypnotherapy of severe Irritable Bowel Syndrome: further experience," *Gut.*, 28: 423-425.

Whorwell, P. J., Prior, A., & Faragher, E. B. (1984). "Controlled trial of hypnotherapy in the treatment of severe refractory Irritable Bowel Syndrome," *Lancet*, 2: 1232-1234.

Winnicott, Donald Woods. (1971). *Playing and Reality.* London: Routledge, 1982.

Winnicott, Donald Woods. (1978). Piggle: an account of the psychoanalytical treatment of a little girl. London: Hogarth Press.

Wyatt, Tristram D. (1956). *Pheromones and Animal Behaviour.* Communication by smell and taste. (2003). New York: Cambridge University Press.

Yehouda, R. (1995). "Low urinary cortisol excretion in Holocaust survivors with post-traumatic stress disorders," *American Journal of Psychiatry*, 152: 982-996.

Zeigarnik, B. (1927). "Das behalten erledigter und unerledigter handlungen," *Psychologische Forschung*, 9, p. 1-85, summarized in "On finished and unfinished tasks," in W.D. Ellis, *A Source Book of Gestalt Psychology.* New York: Harcourt Brace, 1938.

Books published in English
by Gestalt Institute Press:

Suffering In Silence
by Anne Schutzenberger and Ghislain Devroede
with Foreword by Anne Teachworth

Why We Pick The Mates We Do
by Anne Teachworth
with Foreword by Anne Schutzenberger

Those Who Come After
by Renate Perls with Eileen Ain
with Foreword by Richard Kitzler

A Funny Thing Happened
on the Way to Enlightenment
by Lenny Ravich
with Foreword by Anne Teachworth

The Bridge: Dialogues Across Cultures
Edited by Talia Levine Bar-Yoseph
with Foreword by Mackie Blanton

You can order any of these books at
$20 each USD plus $4 shipping and handling
inside the USA or $8 outside.

Contact ateachw@aol.com or go to
www.gestaltinstitutepress.com
504.828.2267 or 1.800.786.1065

CPSIA information can be obtained at www.ICGtesting.com
Printed in the USA
LVOW132015230812

295676LV00002B/19/A

9 781889 968513